SOCCER BRAIN

The Ultimate Football Quiz Book

SOCCER BRAIN

The Ultimate Football Quiz Book

Dave Ball and Gavin Buckland

Milo Books

First published in Great Britain in 2001 by Milo Books
in association with Granada Media Commercial Ventures Ltd

Copyright © Granada Media Group Limited 2001

Soccer Brain is a North Star production for Granada Television Ltd

ISBN 1 903854 01 6

Typeset by Avon DataSet Ltd, Bidford on Avon, Warks
www.avondataset.com

Printed and bound in Great Britain by Guernsey Press Co Ltd, Guernsey

Sold and distributed in Great Britain by Turnaround Publisher Services Ltd,
Unit 3, Olympia Trading Estate, Coburg Road, London N22 6TZ
Tel 020 8829 3000

MILO BOOKS
P. O. Box 153, Bury, Lancs BL0 9FX
info@milobooks.com

Our two authors have set the questions for Granada Television's *Soccer Brain* series, as well as many other TV and radio sporting quizzes.

David Ball is regarded as one of the country's leading sporting experts. A long-standing member of the BBC Television *A Question of Sport* production team, he is also a former BBC Brain of Sport.

Gavin Buckland has been the Merseyside Sports Quiz champion for the past decade and also works on *A Question of Sport*.

Contents

Introduction

Welcome to the ultimate test of your football knowledge. We aim to sort out the David Beckhams of the trivia business from those who are purely Sunday League subs' bench material. But hopefully – with around 3,000 questions – there is enough for everybody to make even the longest away journey seem tolerable.

Soccer Brain was initially conceived as a literary companion to the successful Granada television series of the same name. But while the television series aims to find the leading soccer expert in the North-West of England, this book is aimed at football fans everywhere in the country and has a truly nationwide feel.

The book is split into 15 separate matches, with each having questions for two players. So you can play against a pal, or simply take turns with a group of friends. The games are split into six rounds (with 15 questions per round for each player) and that nice referee has decided to add on a bit of injury-time at the end, to give the player lagging behind a chance to catch up. The format is simple: the player who provides the most correct answers is the winner. If there is a draw after extra-time, then we go to the heart-stopping penalty shoot-out, but if you do please make sure the referee's not from Belgium (see the end of Round 13).

Round 1 – British Clubs

The intention of this round is to test your knowledge of British football from the formation of the Football League to the present day (don't worry, most names should be familiar). After a few early 'looseners' the questions, as in all the other rounds, should get tougher as you progress.

Round 2 – The Derby Match

The two players answer questions on clubs with a local rivalry. For example one player will answer questions on Liverpool whilst the other takes Everton (other rivalries include Manchester City and United, Arsenal v Tottenham, Rangers v Celtic, etc).

Round 3 – British Cups

Each player answers questions on British Cup competitions. Most rounds have a specific Cup theme (the League Cup or FA Cup) or are time-based (the 1970s or 1980s). For simplicity, the League Cup is called exactly that in this section and not given the name of its many sponsors.

Round 4 – The European Game
The two players tackle questions on the game on the Continent, with a few rounds on English clubs abroad thrown in. The aim is to provide a balance for each game: for example, one player tackles questions on Italian clubs whilst the other takes on those from Spain. Note that the European Champions League is called the European (or European Champions) Cup.

Round 5 – The International Game
Each player is quizzed on international football. Again the intention is to provide some sort of rivalry, so one player may face 15 questions on Scotland whilst the other does the same for England.

Round 6 – Quickfire
As we enter the final 15 minutes, things get a bit frantic, with each player facing questions on any football subject.

Injury Time – The Group Phase
Each player faces three questions, with each having several answers. And with a total number of 12 points available, scorelines can change dramatically. The questions can be on any football subject.

The Penalty Shoot-out
At this point, if both players are level, then each answers five questions with the highest scorer being declared the winner. If things are still level, then the match is declared a draw and a replay should be arranged (but at least you don't have to wait ten days).

Full-time
After the inquest has been completed – with the loser kept behind in the dressing room for an hour, of course – and all the TV interviews done, then both players can get some post-match entertainment from a few weird and wonderful stories, trivia and quotes from the game. Here you can find out what happens to a football kit when it is accidentally washed in curry powder; what the announcer at the Bristol derby said over the tannoy that got him sacked; the 'Group of Death' where all the matches were drawn 1–1; and Harry Redknapp's pillow talk that led to a win at Chelsea . . .

So let's put the coats down and let battle commence!

SOCCER BRAIN

Questions

BRITISH CLUBS

1.   Which club is known as 'The Gunners'?

2.   Against which club was Man Utd playing when the sent-off Eric Cantona launched his infamous 'kung fu' kick?

3.   Who is the only player to score in three different FA Cup finals at Wembley?

4.   Which Division One club were knocked out of the Worthington Cup in 2000–2001 by Liverpool in the Semi Final?

5.   Who was the manager of Sheffield Wednesday between 1983 and 1988?

6.   Which club did Bobby Robson manage to an FA Cup final win?

7.   Which QPR player scored a hat trick against Forest and then Everton over the Easter weekend in 1993?

8.   Which was the only side Everton defeated in an FA Cup final in the 1980s?

9.   Which famous player appeared under Bill Shankly for Huddersfield, Matt Busby at Man Utd and Jock Stein for Scotland?

10. Which club lost in the play-offs in 1998–9 but defeated Wigan at Wembley in 1999–2000 to win promotion to Division One?

11. Blackpool provided one player in England's World Cup-winning side in 1966 – who was he?

12. Who played in the 1990 FA Cup Final and the 2000 Scottish Cup Final and won 91 Scottish caps in total?

13. Which player has scored in Premiership defeats of Man Utd whilst at Sheffield United, Leeds United and Middlesbrough?

14. Besides Arsenal which other League club did both Lee Dixon and Steve Bould play for?

15. For which club did 1970s star Tony Currie once play in an FA Cup Final?

BRITISH CLUBS

1. Which former England striker has played for West Ham, Everton and Leicester and played for Barnet in 2001?

2. Who is the 'colourful' manager of Peterborough United ?

3. Plymouth Argyle are one of the few clubs in Britain to play in which colour shirts in home games?

4. Who was the first player to score 100 Premier League goals?

5. Glenn Hoddle managed which club before Chelsea and England?

6. By which nickname did Paul Ince like to be called?

7. Which club in 1998–9 won the First Division with 105 points?

8. Which club won the Championship in the 1990s yet the following season failed to win away from home?

9. Who was the first goalkeeper to win League Championship medals with two different clubs, doing so in 1989 and 1992?

10. Which Premiership striker in the 2000–2001 season has played for four teams which have won the European Cup – Liverpool, Aston Villa, Nottingham Forest and Benfica?

11. Which club finished third in the Premiership in 1994–95 after being promoted from Division One?

12. He once played for Tranmere and held the Northern Ireland record of 13 goals from 38 games – who is he?

13. Which Welsh club have been managed by Terry Yorath, Phil Neal and Russell Osman?

14. Name the last club to win an FA Cup Final replay?

15. Name either of the Nigerians who gained seven caps for their country whilst at Leyton Orient?

MANCHESTER CITY

1. Which former City player is now the manager of the Republic of Ireland?

2. Who was the first player to score a hat trick in the Premiership in 2000–1?

3. Which former Man United favourite scored the goal which condemned them to Division Two in 1974, as City won the derby 1–0?

4. Which current Sunderland forward had a short spell with Manchester City?

5. Which German was City's leading goalscorer in the Premiership in 1994–5 and 1995–6?

6. Against which side did City pull back two late goals before winning a penalty shoot out in the 1999 Second Division play-off final?

7. Which former England winger played for Manchester United in their three FA Cup finals 1976, 77 and 79 and had a short spell as City manager?

8. Who scored 13 penalties for City in the 1971–2 season and later became club chairman?

9. Which City forward won his only England cap against Spain in 1992?

10. Who began his career at Maine Road and scored 141 league goals for Oldham between 1980–1994 – a club record?

11. In which city did Man City win the European Cup Winners Cup?

12. Against which club did three City players each score hat-tricks in the same league game in 1987?

13. Nicknamed 'Nijinsky', he is still City's most capped England International with 48 caps. Who is he?

14. The mother and father were Olympic medallists, the sons played for City in recent years – who are they?

15. City sold two of their stars, Gary Owen and Peter Barnes, to which club?

MANCHESTER UNITED

1. Which club knocked defending champions Manchester Utd out of the Champions Cup in 1999–2000?

2. Which club did United defeat to win their first European Cup final?

3. Who is the only player to captain his club to victory in three FA Cup finals?

4. From which club did the Reds sign Jaap Stam?

5. Who was the first post-war player to score both for and against United in a league game with Liverpool?

6. Who in recent years became the last player to rejoin United, doing so on a Bosman transfer?

7. Two Dutchmen have won FA Cup winner's medals with Manchester United, Jaap Stam and which man in 1983?

8. In September 1990 which former United player scored a hat trick in Liverpool's 4–0 win at Anfield?

9. Which current United defender started his career with 72 league appearances for Leeds United?

10. When Manchester United signed Bryan Robson in 1981, which other West Brom player came to the club as part of the deal?

11. Which club did United defeat at Old Trafford on the final day of the 1998–99 season to clinch the title?

12. Who missed a penalty at Old Trafford in 2000 for Middlesbrough, the first awarded against United at home in the league since December 1993?

13. Whose goal in a third round FA Cup tie in 1990 effectively saved Alex Ferguson's career at Old Trafford?

14. Who in 1992 retired from international football after 26 goals in his 90 England appearances?

15. Who joined the club in 1972 and captained United's only FA Cup-winning side of the 1970s?

FA CUP - GENERAL

1. Who knocked the holders Chelsea out of the competition in the fifth round in 2000–1?

2. On what midweek night were FA Cup final replays held during the 1980s and 1990s?

3. Which club lost both their semi-finals in the 1990s – to Sheffield Wednesday in 1993 and Newcastle United in 1998?

4. Which man captained Everton in four FA Cup finals in the 1980s – the only man to do so at Wembley?

5. In 1985 who became the first man to be sent-off in Wembley Cup final history?

6. Which club in 1957 and 1958 were the first to lose FA Cup finals at Wembley in consecutive seasons?

7. How did Eddie Kelly's goal in the 1971 final make Cup final history?

8. Which international lost all four of his FA Cup semi-finals in the 1990s – one with Portsmouth and three with Spurs?

9. Which Scotland international kept goal for Leeds United in three of their FA Cup finals of the 1970s?

10. Jimmy Melia managed which FA Cup final team in the 1980s?

11. How did Darlington's defeat by Aston Villa by 4–1 in the third round in 1999–2000 make FA Cup history?

12. Which Manchester City goalkeeper broke his neck in the 1956 final but continued playing until the end of the match?

13. Which famous player captained Spurs to FA Cup glory in both 1961 and 1962?

14. Who managed a side in an FA Cup match at Wembley for the first time in 22 years in 2000?

15. Which Arsenal player in the 1990s scored the latest ever goal in Cup final history, in the last minute of extra-time of the replay?

8

THE CUPS – GENERAL

1. Which player scored for Manchester United in both the 1992 League Cup final and 1994 FA Cup final?

2. When Wycombe Wanderers knocked Wimbledon out of the FA Cup on penalties in the fifth round in 2001, who was the former Dons star who was their manager?

3. Who managed different sides in the League Cup final in both 1993 and 2001?

4. Who was the Republic of Ireland international who was the last player to score in consecutive League Cup finals – for Liverpool in 1982 and 1983?

5. Which current Premiership ground staged the FA Cup final in the three years prior to Wembley staging its first final in 1923?

6. He scored for Liverpool in the 1989 FA Cup final and was the Tranmere manager in the 2000 League Cup final – who is he?

7. Which Brighton player is immortalised in Peter Jones's commentary of the last minute of extra-time in the 1983 Cup final at Wembley, when he appeared certain to score but had his shot saved?

8. Who by playing for Sheffield Wednesday in 1993 became the first Swede to appear in an FA Cup final?

9. Who scored in the 1980 League Cup final for Wolves and the 1984 FA Cup final for Everton?

10. Which club defeated Fulham 10–0 in the League Cup in a second round, first leg match in 1986–87?

11. Whose appearance for Liverpool in the 2001 final meant he had played in four out of the last five finals of the competition, going back to 1997?

12. League Champions in 1978, who trounced Ipswich Town 5–0 in the 1978 Charity Shield to record the biggest ever victory in the match at Wembley?

13. Which Third Division side shocked Arsenal 3–1 in the 1969 League Cup final with Don Rogers scoring twice?

14. Which 18-year-old played for Nottingham Forest in the 1978 League Cup final against Liverpool despite never playing for Forest in a League match in his career?

15. Which player, by scoring for Aston Villa in the 1957 FA Cup final and the 1961 League Cup final, became the first player to score in both finals?

EUROPEAN CHAMPIONS CUP

1. Which club won the first five European Cup Finals from 1956–60?

2. Who captained Man United when they won the competition in 1968?

3. Who managed Liverpool when they won the trophy in 1984?

4. Which club became the first side to lose in consecutive finals, doing so in 1998 and 1999?

5. Which England international played for Marseille in the 1991 final?

6. In 1995 who became the first Englishman to score a hat-trick in a Champions League match, doing so for Blackburn against Rosenberg?

7. When AC Milan beat Steaua Bucharest 4–0 in the 1989 Final, which future Premiership manager scored twice for the Italians?

8. In the 2000–1 Champions League, which side inflicted Arsenal's heaviest ever away defeat in Europe by 4–1, having inflicted their heaviest European defeat at Highbury by 5–2 in 1982?

9. Which English club went out of the European Cup in 1975–76, against Real Madrid, despite winning the first leg by 4–1?

10. Which German club won the trophy for the only time in 1983 against Juventus?

11. Which country staged the final in 2000?

12. Which legendary player scored 49 goals for Real Madrid in the competition?

13. Which defender was the only player to appear in all five of Liverpool's finals from 1977–85?

14. Teams from which city played in the Finals of 1966 and 1991?

15. Which side did Sven Goran Eriksson manage in the 1990 Final against AC Milan?

EUROPEAN CHAMPIONS CUP

1. Which side won the European Cup for the first time against Malmo in 1979?

2. In the 1997 final which future Liverpool and Fulham player scored twice for the winners Borussia Dortmund?

3. Which England international has played for Leeds, Blackburn and Newcastle United in the Champions Cup?

4. Who scored Manchester United's first European hat-trick for 29 years in the Champions Cup match against Feyenoord in 1997?

5. Who captained Juventus to victory in the 1996 final before moving to England to play in the Premiership?

6. Who scored in both legs for Rangers when they beat Leeds in the second round in 1991–92?

7. Which French side reached the final for the only time when losing to Bayern Munich in 1976?

8. In which city did Liverpool win two of their European Cup Finals?

9. Which Manchester United player is the only player to have scored in an FA Cup Final and European Cup final?

10. Two clubs from which city won the competition in three consecutive years from 1963 to 1965?

11. Which is the only country to have provided both teams in the final?

12. Who was the former German international sacked as Real Madrid manager immediately after winning the competition in 1998?

13. With which side in 1993 did former Chelsea player Didier Deschamps win the first of his two winner's medals in the competition?

14. In the 1997–98 Champions League, who scored a hat-trick for Newcastle against Barcelona in a 3–2 home victory?

15. Which British city has seen both of its clubs reach the semi-finals of the competition: one in 1963 and the other in 1984?

ENGLAND

1. Who was caretaker manager of England between the reigns of Sir Alf Ramsey and Don Revie in 1974?

2. Apart from Gary Lineker which other player scored for England in the 1986 World Cup finals – doing so against Paraguay?

3. Who played his first international for England in 1970 and the last 20 years later?

4. Against which country did Howard Wilkinson take charge of England for the first time in February 1999?

5. Against which country did England play their final international at Wembley?

6. Who scored five times at Wembley in 1975 for England against Cyprus?

7. Which current Newcastle player scored on his England debut against Romania in 1994 at Wembley?

8. Who made 24 appearances in midfield for England from 1986 to 1990 whilst with Aston Villa, Spurs and Nottingham Forest?

9. Which country did England play for the first time on 30 November 1872?

10. Who scored the last goal for England under Kevin Keegan – against France in September 2000?

11. On which Premiership ground did England play an international for the first time against Belgium in October 1999?

12. In 1980 who were the last reigning World Champions to be beaten by England in a full international, 3–1 at Wembley?

13. Which country scored after just nine seconds against England in 1993 only to lose the match 7–1?

14. Which then-Coventry City player made his England debut against Chile at Wembley in February 1998?

15. Which goalkeeper made just one England appearance, keeping a clean sheet against Portugal in 1974?

WORLD CUP - GENERAL

1. Which country won the World Cup for the first time in 1998?

2. Which country knocked England out of the Mexico World Cup finals of 1986 at the quarter-final stages?

3. Who scored Brazil's opening goal in the 1970 World Cup Final against Italy?

4. Which Brighton player appeared for England during the 1982 World Cup?

5. Which country lost in two World Cup Finals in the 1970s?

6. Who was the manager of West Germany when they won the World Cup in 1990?

7. Which African country lost 9–0 to Yugoslavia in the 1974 World Cup?

8. In which country were the finals held for the only time in 1962?

9. Which Italian was the leading goalscorer in Italia '90?

10. The Republic of Ireland were beaten 2–0 by which country in the second round knock-out stage in USA '94?

11. In 1998 who became the first Scotsman sent-off in a World Cup finals match, against Morocco?

12. Later to play club football in Spain, he scored a memorable winning goal for Northern Ireland against the host country in the 1982 World Cup finals?

13. In the 1978 World Cup the eventual champions Argentina were beaten 1–0 by which country in the group stages?

14. Who scored ten goals for Peru in the finals of 1970 and 1978?

15. Which striker was the only player to appear for the Cameroon in the three World Cups of 1990,1994 and 1998?

QUICKFIRE

1. Which former Liverpool favourite has managed Swansea and now manages Kidderminster?

2. Which club lost in an FA Cup final during the 1980s in the same season they were relegated from the top flight?

3. Who was the first player to score 200 goals in the Scottish Premier Division and still hopes to add to his total?

4. Two sides in the Football League have names starting with the letter 'D' – Derby and who else?

5. Wigan and Oldham both share the same nickname – what is it?

6. Who was the last Blackpool player to appear in a full international for England?

7. Which current Sunderland forward helped Arsenal to defeat Liverpool in the 1987 League Cup final?

8. Luis Figo and Joao Pinto scored to bring Portugal back to 2–2 against England in Euro 2000. Who scored Portugal's winner?

9. Which club did John Gregory manage before Aston Villa?

10. Which player retired from football after breaking his leg for Aston Villa against Ipswich Town in the league in 2000?

11. Which club are nicknamed 'the Tractor Boys'?

12. Which TV pundit was banned for the rest of the season in 1987–88 after a foul on Jim Melrose of Shrewsbury whilst with Swindon?

13. Which club beat Blackburn Rovers in the sixth round of the FA Cup in 2000–1 to reach the semi-final for the third time in four years?

14. Where did Celtic play in the 1994–95 season when Parkhead was being renovated?

15. Which England defender's middle names are Sulzeer Jeremiah?

QUICKFIRE

1. Who played for Chelsea in 1999–2000 and appeared in four European Cup Finals for Marseille and Juventus.

2. Now a BBC pundit, he was the last Scottish international to captain his side to victory in an FA Cup final at Wembley – who is he?

3. Two clubs in the English League have names that begin with the letter 'E' – Everton and which other?

4. Who was the last player to play for both sides in the Merseyside derby?

5. Who helped Man Utd to success in the 1990s and played for Man City in 2001?

6. Who is Preston's most capped player with 76 England caps?

7. Which former Northern Ireland player managed Macclesfield Town into the Football League?

8. At which ground did Blackburn clinch the Premiership title in 1994–5?

9. Which player has won a European Cup winner's medal with Borussia Dortmund and a League Cup winner's medal with Spurs?

10. Which England international in 1990–91 received the FIFA fair play award for never having been booked or sent-off in his career?

11. Which current Spurs player has a father who played in their FA Cup-winning side of 1982?

12. In 1992–93 who had to wait until the 971st league game of his career to be sent-off?

13. Which is the oldest surviving league club in Wales?

14. Who scored the only goal of the 1993 European Cup final for Marseille and would later join Rangers?

15. Which Spurs player in the first season of the Premiership was the first player to be sent-off for feigning injury?

The Group phase

1. Which three clubs, who were amongst the twelve clubs
    who founded the Football League in 1888, were also
    founder members of the Premier League in 1992?
    (3 points)

2. Who are the six players born in Denmark to play in a FA
    Cup final?
    (6 points)

3. What are the christian names of the three Wallace brothers
    who played together 25 times for Southampton?
    (3 points)

Penalty Shoot-out

1. Which Premiership player captained the Cameroon to
    victory in the African Nations Cup in 2000?

2. Who between 1964 and 1966 became the first captain to
    lift three different trophies at Wembley in three
    consecutive years?

3. Which North West club, then in Division One, were beaten
    1–0 at home by non-league Wimbledon in the FA Cup in
    1975?

4. Which England international became the most expensive
    player (at £7 million) to move from England to a foreign
    club in July 1995?

5. In August 1970 which Football League club became the
    first side to lose a game on penalties in this country?

Full-time

Real Madrid played a record 122 league matches at home without defeat from February 1957 to March 1965. Atletico Madrid ended the run in 1965 having been the last team to beat their rivals at home eight years earlier.

Harry Redknapp on a victory at Chelsea: 'Last night I was lying in bed with my wife – if you have a husband as ugly as me, you want to talk about football – and she said "Harry, if you are drawing, push Trevor Sinclair up." I gambled and it worked a treat.'

English club sides during the 1990s produced some interesting pairs of players: Holmes and Watson at Everton, Bryant and May at Bristol City. There was Abbott and Costello at Bradford City in the early 1990s, when Irons and Steele played for Tranmere. A 1990 League Cup tie between Blackpool and Spurs saw Bamber and Gascoigne share the same pitch. Real Oviedo in 2001 had Stan and Oli up front after Stan Collymore went on loan to the Spanish side.

The Group phase

1.   For which three Italian clubs did David Platt appear in his
      career?
      (3 points)

2.   Which four African sides, and one Middle East side, did
      England play in the World Cup finals from 1982 to 1998?
      (5 points)

3.   Which four clubs did Ron Atkinson manage in the
      Premiership?
      (4 points)

Penalty Shoot-out

1.   Who left Blackpool in 1967 and went on to captain the
      European Cup winners?

2.   Which North West club won the FA Cup in 1900 and 1903
      and also has the shortest name of any side in the league?

3.   Which famous England centre forward is the youngest
      player to score a hat-trick in the top flight – aged 17 years
      four days in 1936?

4.   Which London club can uniquely claim to have been
      undefeated at home in four different divisions – Divisions
      Two, Three (North and South) and Four?

5.   Who scored England's first goal under both Glenn Hoddle
      and Sven-Goran Eriksson?

Full-time

Crazy days in the Leyland DAF Cup in 1990–91: one group, the 'Group of Death', produced nothing but 1–1 draws and had to be entirely replayed. The draw for the second round produced the following: Burnley or Stockport v Crewe, Burnley or Stockport.

'When seagulls follow the trawler, it is because they think that sardines will be thrown into the sea' – Eric Cantona

'If a Frenchman talks about seagulls, sardines and trawlers he's called a philosopher. I'd just be called a short Scottish bum talking crap' – Gordon Strachan

The shortest career of any England player in the World Cup finals is the six minutes played by Kerry Dixon against Poland in 1986.

BRITISH CLUBS

1. Who are known as 'the Tykes' and play at Oakwell?

2. Andy Payton was the leading scorer in Division Two in 1999–2000, scoring 27 goals for which club?

3. Which goalscoring legend made his Wrexham debut on the opening day of the 1998–9 season?

4. Which man set a new British transfer record of £3.7 million in the summer of 1993?

5. Who has played for both Manchester clubs, Arsenal and Everton and has managed Blackburn?

6. To which club did Trevor Francis move after leaving Nottingham Forest in 1981?

7. On which club's ground is there the Sir Tom Finney Stand and the Bill Shankly Kop?

8. Who was the manager of Swansea City when they played in the top flight in 1981–2?

9. Now a TV pundit, he made his first of his 73 appearances for Preston aged 17 in April 1975?

10. To which Italian side did Watford sell Luther Blissett in 1983?

11. Which member of England's 1966 World Cup winning side was sacked as Chelsea's manager in 1981?

12. Who won a League Championship medal with both Liverpool and Rangers and managed both sides?

13. Which Division Two side play at Dean Court?

14. Only one player managed to score against Everton in the FA Cup run to the final in 1995 – which Spurs player did this in the semi-final?

15. Which club in 1984–5 season lost a record 31 games in the First Division?

BRITISH CLUBS

1.   Which man was in charge of Norwich City when they finished third in the Premiership in 1992–93?

2.   For which club did Peter Thorne score 30 goals in all competitions in 1999–2000?

3.   Which club did Peter Taylor manage prior to joining Leicester City?

4.   Which goalscoring legend ended his career with a brief spell at Burnley in the 1999–2000 season?

5.   Which current Premiership manager has managed a top-flight club in the 1970s, 80s, 90s and now into 2001?

6.   Which current Premiership club is the only side to have won the League Championship once and the FA Cup once?

7.   Who is the only post-war player to win a League Championship medal with both Liverpool and Celtic?

8.   Which future England manager played for Tottenham in the 1967 FA Cup final?

9.   Which manager bought Gordon Hill whilst in charge of Man Utd, Derby County and QPR?

10.   Which man managed Tranmere Rovers in the 1970s, 1980s and 1990s?

11.   Which Premiership club has had only eight managers since 1902?

12.   Which player appeared in FA Cup semi-finals at Wembley for Sheffield Wednesday in 1993 and Bolton Wanderers in 2000?

13.   How did Billy help avert a disaster in the 1923 FA Cup final?

14.   With which club was Keith Edwards playing when he was the League's leading goalscorer in the 1981–82 season?

15.   In the 1993–94 season for which team was Mark Smith playing when he was sent-off after just 19 seconds of a game?

LIVERPOOL

1.   Who scored the goal which ended Man United's unbeaten home league record in 2000–1?

2.   Which Liverpool player was twice voted PFA Young Player of the Year during the 1990s?

3.   Which club defeated Liverpool 4–3 in a league game in 2000–1 but later lost 2–0 in an FA Cup tie?

4.   Which club did Liverpool defeat to win their last trophy at Wembley?

5.   In the 1989 FA Cup Final, Ian Rush scored twice after coming on as a substitute for which future Merseyside club manager?

6.   Who succeeded Bob Paisley as manager of the club?

7.   Who was the last former Everton player to score for Liverpool in the Merseyside derby?

8.   Against which club did Robbie Fowler once score five goals in a League Cup tie?

9.   Who captained Liverpool to a hat trick of trophies in 1984?

10. Which current Liverpool player holds the record for most England U21 caps and made his full debut in 1999 against Hungary?

11. Besides Roger Hunt which other Anfield favourite played for England in the 1966 World Cup Finals?

12. Which defender scored a rare hat trick for the club in 1986 against Birmingham City?

13. In April 1990 this player scored a hat trick on his full first-team debut for Liverpool against Charlton before joining Tottenham – who is he?

14. Which club have Liverpool been drawn against a record 15 times in the FA Cup?

15. Which defender played in 375 consecutive games for the Reds between 14 December 1975 and 24 September 1983?

EVERTON

1. Which close neighbours knocked the Blues out of the FA Cup in 2000–1 by 3–0 at Goodison?

2. Who left Man Utd and teamed up with Walter Smith as assistant manager at Goodison?

3. Which player left Everton and joined Fiorentina in February 1997 for a record £8million fee for a winger?

4. Which Welshman captained Everton to their only European success?

5. Who kept goal for the club in four FA Cup finals 1984–1995?

6. Which English international was the club's leading scorer in the league in 1989–90, 1990–91, 1991–92?

7. Which 1985 PFA Footballer of the Year moved to Everton from Bolton in 1982 for just £60,000?

8. Which Everton player was once the most expensive defender in British football when moving from Tottenham to Glasgow Rangers in 1987?

9. Which member of England's Euro 2000 side played in the 1992 tournament whilst with Everton?

10. Who is the only Evertonian to both play in and manage the club to League Championship success?

11. Now with Leeds United, he scored in the first minute of a Merseyside derby in 1998–9 for Everton at Anfield?

12. Who later joined the Goodison club after having played against them in 1984 FA Cup Final?

13. Who in January 1966 became the club's youngest player in a league game and now manages a club in the North West?

14. Who was the only Evertonian to score 30 or more league goals in a season during the 1970s?

15. Which future Everton manager won his only England cap against Malta in 1971?

FA CUP –THE 1970s

1. Which club appeared in consecutive finals in 1972 and 1973?

2. Who was the legendary manager of Liverpool when they won the trophy in 1974?

3. Who scored the only goal of the game in 1973 when Sunderland lifted the trophy?

4. Nicknamed 'Chopper', who captained to Chelsea to victory in the final in 1970?

5. Which player captained Arsenal to victory in 1971 when he was also voted Footballer of the Year?

6. Which Liverpool player was the only player to score in two different Cup finals during the decade – in 1971 and 1974?

7. Later to manage Northern Ireland, he brought short-lived joy to Man United fans by equalising in the 1979 final against Arsenal – who was he?

8. Who appeared in two different Cup-winning teams in the decade – Chelsea in 1970 and Southampton in 1976?

9. Which current Premiership manager starred for Third Division Crystal Palace in their run to the semi-finals in 1976?

10. Which player scored a record nine goals in a first round tie for Bournemouth against Margate in November 1971?

11. Who scored for Leeds in both the 1970 final at Wembley and the replay?

12. Which current First Division side reached the semi-finals twice during the decade and lost on both occasions – in 1973 and 1979?

13. Which current Premiership ground last staged an FA Cup semi-final when Arsenal defeated Orient in 1978?

14. In which year in the decade did only the second all-London FA Cup Final at Wembley take place?

15. Which non-league side reached the fifth round in 1978 before losing a replay to Wrexham at St James Park?

THE CUPS – General

1. Which current manager is the only man to manage the FA Cup final victors on four occasions at Wembley?
2. Which trophy was won at Wembley in 1993 when Cremonese beat Derby County 3–1 in the final?
3. Which non-league side, managed by Geoff Chapple, reached the fourth round of the FA Cup in 2000–1?
4. Which was the last club to win the FA Cup for the first time in their history?
5. Which was the only club to lose FA Cup finals in consecutive seasons during the 1990s?
6. Which Second Division side lost 8–0 at home to eventual winners Liverpool in the League Cup in 2000–1?
7. Who scored a memorable free-kick for Spurs against Arsenal in the 1991 FA Cup semi-final at Wembley?
8. What was the name of the trophy played for between 1970 and 1973 which featured the top two goal scoring clubs from each Division which had not been promoted or were playing in Europe?
9. Who scored for Brighton in the 1983 FA Cup final and then played for Spurs in the 1987 final?
10. Which club knocked Liverpool out of the League Cup in the semi-finals in 1986 only to lose the final 3–0 to Oxford United?
11. For which North West club was Frankie Bunn playing when he scored a League Cup record 6 goals in a match against Scarborough in 1989?
12. Who scored both Manchester United's goals when they defeated Liverpool 2–0 in the Charity Shield at Wembley in 1983?
13. Who during the 1980s and 1990s became the first manager to win the FA Cup or League Cup with three different clubs?
14. Which centre-half scored for Crystal Palace against Liverpool in the 1990 FA Cup semi-final and then opened the scoring in the final against Manchester United?
15. Which current Premiership club appeared in the First Division play-off at Wembley in four out of five seasons from 1992–96?

EUROPEAN CUP WINNERS CUP

1. Who scored the only goal of the game when Arsenal lifted the trophy for the first time in 1994?

2. He was a Premiership manager in the 2000–1 season and played for Aberdeen when they won the trophy in 1983?

3. Which English sides only Final appearance was when they lost 2–1 to Borussia Dortmund in 1966?

4. Which club became the only side from Wales to reach the semi-final of any European competition, when losing 4–3 on aggregate to Hamburg in 1967–68 competition?

5. Which Belgian club reached three consecutive Cup Winners Cup Finals from 1976–78?

6. When Sampdoria defeated Anderlecht 2–0 in the 1990 Final which future Chelsea player scored both goals?

7. On the way to winning the trophy in 1991 which Welsh side did Man United defeat 5–0 on aggregate in the second round?

8. Who was the manager of Barcelona when they lifted the trophy in 1997?

9. When Ajax won the competition in 1987, who was the former Ipswich Town player in their side?

10. Who was sent-off six minutes from time for Chelsea in their victory over Stuttgart in 1998?

11. Which British club won the competition for the only time against Moscow Dynamo in 1972?

12. Which Danish player's goal in the 1982 final for Barcelona meant that he would go down in history as the only player to score in the finals of the three major European competitions?

13. Chelsea won the trophy in 1971 against Real Madrid after a replay; which player scored for the Blues in both matches?

14. Later to win the European Cup, which German side won the Cup Winners Cup in 1977?

15. Who was the famous Austrian forward who scored for Barcelona in the 1979 Final and for Rapid Vienna in the Final against Everton six years later?

EUROPEAN CHAMPIONS CUP

1. Four teams from which country played in the Champions Cup in 2000–01?

2. When Manchester United won the trophy in 1998–99 which side did they beat 4–3 on aggregate in the semi-final?

3. Which player scored the winning goal for Liverpool against Real Madrid in 1981 and the winning penalty against Roma in 1984?

4. Which Greek side knocked Everton out of the quarter-finals in 1970–71 before losing 2–0 to Ajax in the Final?

5. In the 2000–1 Champions Cup which Austrian side finished top of their first round group despite losing 5–0 to both Rangers and Monaco?

6. Apart from Benfica, which is the only other Portugese side to have won the Cup, doing so in 1987?

7. Who, when managing Leeds United in 1975, became the first Englishman to manage a team in the Final?

8. Who scored for Celtic in both of their Finals in 1967 and 1970, the first British player to achieve this feat?

9. In 1996–97 Manchester United reached the semi-finals for the first time under Sir Alex Ferguson, but lost 2–0 on aggregate to which side?

10. Which side knocked Chelsea out of the Champions Cup at the quarter-final stage in 1999–2000 despite losing 3–1 at Stamford Bridge?

11. Who scored the only goal of the game when Liverpool beat Bruges at Wembley in the 1978 final?

12. Two players in the victorious Real Madrid side in 2000 had come from Premiership clubs the previous year – Steve McManaman and who else?

13. Which Frenchman, formerly a European Footballer of the Year, won loser's medals with both Marseille in 1991 and AC Milan in 1993?

14. Who scored all four goals for AC Milan when they beat Gothenburg 4–0 in a Champions League match in 1992?

15. Who when playing for Leeds (1975) and Nottingham Forest (1980) is the only man to play for two different English sides in the final of the competition?

EURO 96

1. Whose only goals for England in the tournament were in the 4–1 win over Holland?

2. Who scored a penalty for the Czech Republic in the final against Germany?

3. Apart from Steve Howey, which other Newcastle player was included in the England squad but did not appear in the tournament?

4. Who was the top scorer in the tournament with five goals?

5. Which future Man United player scored the only goal for the Czech Republic against Portugal in the quarter-final?

6. Who was the manager of the eventual winners Germany?

7. Which player appeared in all of England's matches apart from the semi-final against Germany when he was suspended?

8. Who was Scotland's keeper in their three games in the competition?

9. Who was the German keeper who saved Gareth Southgate's penalty in the semi- final against England?

10. He would later join Man United and scored Holland's opening goal of the tournament against Switzerland?

11. Which Liverpool player came on as a substitute for Stuart Pearce against Scotland only to be replaced himself due to injury near the end?

12. What was unique in the tournament about Hristo Stoichkov's goal for Bulgaria against France?

13. Apart from Stuart Pearce who was the other Nottingham Forest player who appeared for England in the Finals?

14. With which Italian club side was Germany's hero in the final, Oliver Bierhoff, based?

15. Which Italian player's missed penalty proved crucial in their 0–0 draw against Germany, resulting in their elimination from the tournament?

EURO 2000

1. Against which country did Alan Shearer score his final international goal?

2. In the group matches which side did not score a goal or point in their three games?

3. Which Dutchman scored five goals in Euro 2000 including a hat-trick?

4. Who was the current Arsenal player who scored for France in the Final?

5. The eventual winners France lost 3–2 to which country in the group stages?

6. Which Liverpool player made his only England appearance of Euro 2000 in the match against Germany as a substitute?

7. Who was the manager of Italy who resigned after the Final?

8. In their semi-final which Dutch player made history by missing a penalty in both normal time and also in the shoot-out?

9. Who kept goal for England in the infamous match against Romania?

10. Who was the Coventry City player who kept goal for Sweden in all three of their group matches?

11. Whose controversial handball led to France scoring the winning penalty against Portugal in their semi-finals?

12. Which country led Yugoslavia 3–0 in their group match only to see the game finish 3–3?

13. Which striker scored both of Turkey's goals when they beat Belgium 2–0 in the group stages?

14. Who was the only English referee used during Euro 2000?

15. Who was the coach of Euro 2000 winners France?

QUICKFIRE

1. Who are the Seagulls who play at Withdean Stadium?

2. Which striker moved from Rangers to Everton for £4 million in December 1994?

3. David Moyes was the Second Division Manager of the Year in 1999–2000. Which club did he lead to promotion?

4. Which 'on loan' goalkeeper famously scored the last gasp goal which kept Carlisle in the league and relegated Scarborough?

5. Which was the last country to lose to Brazil in a World Cup Final?

6. In the 1985–6 season which Everton player won both the PFA and Football Writers' awards for Player of the Year?

7. Name the Scottish international forward who played for Elgin, Shrewsbury, Bury, Millwall and Bolton?

8. Which club was the first in England to spend £1 million on a player in 1979?

9. Which Liverpool player has scored the fastest hat trick in the Premiership taking only four minutes 33 seconds?

10. Who in the Charity Shield in 2000 was the last player sent off at Wembley?

11. Only two countries have won the World Cup on just one occasion, France and which other country?

12. Which Dutchman won a European Cup winner's medal with Ajax in 1995 and Real Madrid in 1998?

13. Which side in 1965 won the Championship on goal average?

14. Which German international played against Liverpool in two European Cup finals?

15. Bobby Tambling, with 164 goals, is the leading goalscorer in the history of which Premiership club?

QUICKFIRE

1. Who are 'the Bees' who play at Griffin Park?

2. On the day Blackburn won the Premiership in 1995 which team drew with Manchester United, thus preventing them from winning the title?

3. Which current Premiership manager was Scotland's part-time manager for the duration of the 1986 World Cup Finals?

4. Which club was relegated from the top division in England for the first time in 1999–2000?

5. Who managed Luton Town from 1978–1986 and from 1991–5?

6. Which was the last English team to win a hat-trick of League Championships, prior to the 2000–1 season?

7. Which England defender won Championship medals with Everton and Rangers in the 80s and went on to play at Tranmere Rovers?

8. Which Dutchman won a European Cup Winners Cup medal with PSV Eindhoven in 1988 and Barcelona in 1992?

9. Who was the only player to score a penalty against England in the 1966 World Cup?

10. Which former Manchester United player was part of Brian Kidd's coaching staff at Blackburn Rovers?

11. At which ground did Leeds United win 3–2 at the end of the 1991–92 season to effectively clinch the title?

12. Which player, who was born in Sierra Leone, appeared for Sheffield Wednesday in the 1993 FA Cup final and would later join Nottingham Forest?

13. Which England player in the 1990 World Cup finals was with a French side at the time?

14. What is the surname of the father and son, one of whom kept goal for Ipswich in their title-winning side of 1962, the other who played in Manchester United's FA Cup-winning sides of 1983 and 1985?

15. Which referee controversially disallowed a Brazilian goal in the 1978 World Cup, as he had already blown for full-time?

The Group phase

1. Which three members of England's 1966 World Cup winning side did not appear in a FA Cup final during their career?
   (3 points)

2. At the start of the 2000–1 season which five players had Manchester United bought for £5 million or more?
   (5 points)

3. Who are the four Spurs players, since 1960, to have each been the leading goalscorer in a season in the top division?
   (4 points)

Penalty Shoot-out

1. Who were the brothers who played in Holland's 1988 European Championship victory?

2. The Mariners have been managed by Bill Shankly and Lawrie McMenemy – who are they?

3. Which British club did Liverpool defeat to enter their first European final in 1966?

4. Who won League Championship winner's medals with Leeds in 1992 and Blackburn Rovers in 1995?

5. Who succeeded Don Revie as England manager in 1977?

Full-time

It was appropriate that Peter Taylor was appointed England coach – albeit temporarily – in 2000 as he was the only man to have been a team-mate of the previous three managers in their playing days. He appeared with Terry Venables at Crystal Palace, Glenn Hoddle at Spurs and Kevin Keegan for England.

Well-known chairman of a top league club in the 1970s, on their club's European draw: 'We've been drawn against Standard Liege of Belgium . . . with the first leg in Standard.'

When Berwick Rangers produced one of the all time great shocks in Scottish football in 1967 by beating Glasgow Rangers 1–0 in the Cup, their goal-keeping hero was non-other than future Rangers managerial legend Jock Wallace. When Wallace became manager of Seville in the 1980s he joked it was because it was the only place were he could find 'eleven good Orangemen'.

The Group phase

1. Which three men were official managers of Wales between the reigns of Terry Yorath and Mark Hughes?
   (3 points)

2. Which six England players since 1980 have been capped whilst playing for Glasgow Rangers?
   (6 points)

3. Only three managers – who have all managed in the Premiership – in the history of the English game have managed clubs in over 1,000 league matches. Who are they?
   (3 points)

Penalty Shoot-out

1. Which was the last country to play in three consecutive World Cup Finals ?

2. Who scored Tranmere's goal against Leicester City in the 2000 League Cup final?

3. Which club was banned from the League Cup in 1986 after banning away fans from their ground following a riot by Millwall fans?

4. How did Argentinian's Pedro Monzon and Gustavo Dezotti create World Cup history in 1990?

5. Which West Ham player retired in 1999 to take up competitive golf ?

Full-time

A whole chapter could be written about trivia relating to Welsh manager Mark Hughes:

— the only man to win four FA Cup winner's medals at Wembley

— in 1991 he became the first player to be voted PFA Player of the Year twice

— the only man to play in the Premiership whilst an international manager

— in 1993–94 he achieved the unique feat of scoring at Wembley in four different games for Manchester United (FA Cup semi-final and final, League Cup final and the Charity Shield)

— on 11 November 1987 he became the only player ever to play in two countries on the same day, playing for Wales in Czechoslovakia and then in Germany for Bayern Munich.

BRITISH CLUBS

1. Three players with the same surname were included Sven Goran Eriksson's first English squad – what was the name?

2. Which current Manchester United player had a loan spell with Preston at one stage of his career?

3. Who was the last Everton player to score in an FA Cup final?

4. On which ground did Stoke City play up to 1997?

5. Which club replaced Chester in the Third Division after winning the Conference in 1999–2000?

6. Which former manager claimed to have had more clubs than Jack Nicklaus?

7. Alan Cork has made the most league appearances and scored the most league goals for which club?

8. Who was the last Englishman to be named European Footballer of the Year?

9. Which Premiership side defeated Manchester Utd 6–3 in the 1996–7 season?

10. Who are the father and son, the father once managed Everton and his son played for Tottenham and England?

11. Who played for Leyton Orient in his 1000th league game at the age of 47 years?

12. Which was the first London club to win the First Division title?

13. Which Wolves player was the last man to score over 50 goals in a season, doing so in the 1980s?

14. Which Stoke City player won eight caps for England from 1982–4?

15. Which current Nationwide Division One club were last champions of England in 1959?

BRITISH CLUBS

1. Which First Division club reached the Worthington Cup final in 2001?

2. Where did Arsenal play their home games in the Champions League in 1998–99?

3. Who was voted Carling Premiership Manager of the Month for August 2000 at the age of 67?

4. Which player received his marching orders for pushing referee Paul Alcock?

5. In the early part of the 2000–1 season which club had two players sent off in a Premiership game against Arsenal at Highbury?

6. Who received the M.B.E in 1998 after being Crewe manager for 15 years?

7. Who made 394 consecutive appearances in a nine-year run from 1981 with Wimbledon, Newcastle and Chelsea?

8. Who was the last man to manage different sides to old First Division-Premiership success?

9. With which club did John Barnes begin his league career in 1981?

10. For which North West club did Ian Wood make a record 525 league appearances from 1966–1980?

11. Who was manager of Stoke City between 1960 and 1977?

12. Which club gained only 52 points in winning their only League Championship in 1955?

13. Name the Reading striker who scored 35 goals in 46 Division Two games in 1993–4?

14. Which Scottish club play at Tannadice Park?

15. Which was the last British club to play a European tie at Prenton Park?

TOTTENHAM HOTSPUR

1. Which Tottenham player had a header disallowed in the game against Argentina in France 1998?

2. Who captained Tottenham in their last FA Cup final appearance at Wembley in 1991?

3. Who was the player who scored a last minute winner against Leicester City in the 1999 Worthington Cup final?

4. Which was the first club to beat Tottenham in an FA Cup final at Wembley?

5. Who won his first England cap in the Euro 2000 qualifiers defeat of Poland and had just left Blackburn for Tottenham?

6. Which Spurs player was elected Footballer of the Year by both the Players and Writers in 1987?

7. Which Tottenham defender was sent off in a League Cup final against Leicester City at Wembley?

8. Who was the Tottenham hero in the 1984 UEFA Cup Final when he kept goal in the penalty shoot out?

9. Which goalkeeper scored a goal in the 1967 Charity Shield?

10. Who was Tottenham's manager when they won successive FA Cup Finals in the 1980s?

11. Who was the club's leading scorer in four of the first five Premiership seasons from 1992–3?

12. In May 1998 Jurgen Klinsmann scored four times in a Premiership game – who was this against?

13. Who captained the club when they won their first European trophy in 1963?

14. In October 1977 Tottenham recorded their biggest league win, when they defeated which club 9–0 on *Match of the Day*?

15. Which father and son played in the FA Cup final for the club in 1961 and 1987 respectively?

ARSENAL

1. Which player set up the winner in the Euro 2000 Final and then joined Arsenal from Marseille?

2. Which Croatian starred in the 1998 World Cup Finals before moving to Highbury?

3. Who in the 1997–8 season broke Cliff Bastin's record to become Arsenal's highest ever goalscorer?

4. Which teenager scored for the club in their FA Cup final win in 1998 over Newcastle?

5. Two men have managed both Tottenham and Arsenal – George Graham and who else?

6. Which Scottish international forward moved from Celtic to Arsenal for a fee of £650,000 in 1983?

7. Who was the club's top scorer when they won the league in 1989 and 1991?

8. Who played for three Italian clubs in the 1990s and won an FA Cup winners and League Championship medal in 1998?

9. Which current Premiership manager appeared in a record 558 appearances for the Gunners?

10. Who won 42 England caps between 1978–1986 while with Nottingham Forest, Cologne and finally Arsenal?

11. Which current Arsenal player has won an Olympic gold medal and also a European Champions Cup winners medal?

12. Against which club, no longer in existence, did Arsenal both gain their biggest win and also suffer their biggest loss?

13. Which former Arsenal defender was twice caretaker manager of the club in the 1990s?

14. Who scored the winning goal for Arsenal in the North London derby FA Cup semi-final at Wembley in 1993?

15. In 1990–91 Arsenal went 17 games unbeaten from the start of the season until losing 6–2 at Highbury in the League Cup against which club?

LEAGUE CUP

1. In 2000–1 which side reached the semi-final of the competition after knocking out the holders Leicester City on the way?

2. In the 1998 final which England international made his Middlesbrough debut against Chelsea?

3. Who scored twice for Aston Villa in the 1977 final and was their manager when they won the trophy in 1996?

4. Who scored both Liverpool's goals in the final when they won the trophy against Bolton in 1995?

5. Which forward won his first domestic honour, 17 years after making his League debut, when playing for Leicester City in 2000?

6. Which club won their first ever trophy by defeating Arsenal 1–0 in 1968?

7. Which man kept goal for Liverpool in the 1981 final against West Ham and then played against them for Spurs in 1982?

8. Which England international goalkeeper played in the final in three different decades, the 1970s, 1980s and 1990s, for three different clubs?

9. Which Republic of Ireland international's goal gave Sheffield Wednesday the trophy in 1991?

10. What first was achieved when Arsenal beat Liverpool in the 1987 final after Ian Rush had opened the scoring?

11. Who scored the winner for Arsenal in the 1993 final against Sheffield Wednesday then broke his arm in the post match celebrations?

12. Which future TV pundit scored for QPR in a Man of the Match performance against West Brom in the 1967 final?

13. Who kept goal for Manchester United in the 1991 final after replacing Jim Leighton in goal for an FA Cup final replay in 1990?

14. Which club, managed by Dave Jones, were the last from the Second Division to reach the semis – doing so in 1997?

15. Who missed a penalty for Aston Villa in the 1975 final but netted the rebound for the only goal of the game?

FA CUP – THE 80s

1. Who when scoring for Manchester United in 1983 became the first player to score for different clubs in Wembley finals, having scored for Arsenal in 1979?

2. Who scored a goal in 1981 that was recently voted the best in an FA Cup final at Wembley?

3. Which Tottenham player scored after just 49 seconds of the 1987 final against Coventry?

4. Which side did Arsenal beat after three replays in their 1980 semi-final?

5. Who was the manager of Wimbledon when they won the Cup in 1988?

6. Who was the Brighton captain who missed the 1983 final through suspension but returned for the replay?

7. Which year of the 1980s saw a Wembley first when the top two clubs in that season's Championship also played each other in the Cup final?

8. Who was the only manager to win the FA Cup in both the 1970s and 1980s?

9. Who during the decade became the first goalkeeper to lift the FA Cup as a captain?

10. Which Manchester City player is credited with scoring at both ends in the first Manchester City-Spurs final in 1981 in a 1–1 draw?

11. Who captained Spurs when they won the FA Cup in both 1981 and 1982?

12. He scored five goals for Coventry City in their FA Cup winning campaign in 1987, including a memorable diving header in the final?

13. In the 1988–89 season which club inflicted Manchester United's last defeat, in open play, at Old Trafford in the FA Cup prior to 2001?

14. Which Republic of Ireland international captained Liverpool when they won the Cup in 1989?

15. Which midfielder played for Brighton in the 1983 final against Manchester United having scored against United in the final for Liverpool six years earlier?

UEFA CUP

1. What change to the final of the competition was made in 1998?

2. Who played for Parma when they won the trophy in 1999 having previously left them to join Newcastle United in 1996?

3. Which English side did Red Star Belgrade knock out of the competition in 2000–1?

4. Who scored both Liverpool's goals in their 2–0 win against Roma in the Italian capital in the fourth round in February 2001?

5. When Spurs won the first leg of the final 2–1 against Wolves in 1972 which England striker scored both goals?

6. Which English side, in Division One in 2000–1, last appeared in the competition in 1995–96 but went out on aggregate to Bayern Munich in the quarter-finals?

7. Which Brazilian international striker scored in both legs for Napoli when they won the 1989 final?

8. Who were the Spanish club who retained the trophy in 1986, the first to do so since 1963?

9. Which Italian side won the UEFA Cup three times during the 1990s?

10. Which Scottish international and current Newcastle United player appeared for Dundee United in the 1987 UEFA Cup final?

11. Who was the only Arsenal player to score in their penalty shoot-out defeat in the 2000 UEFA Cup final?

12. When Liverpool won the competition in 1973 which English side did they beat on away goals in the semi-finals?

13. Which Chilean international scored for Inter Milan in the finals of both 1997 and 1998?

14. Which Manchester United star was top scorer in the 1964–65 tournament with 8 goals?

15. Later to manage Real Madrid, when playing for Borussia Moenchengladbach he scored twice against Liverpool in the 1973 final and a hat-trick against Twente Enschede of Holland in the 1975 final. Who is he?

EUROPEAN CLUBS – General

1. There are a recognised 'big three' sides in Portugese football – Benfica, Porto and which other club?

2. Which Italian side was founded after the merger of two clubs in 1946 – Sampierdaranese and Andrea Doria?

3. Which Dutchman was voted European Footballer of the Year in 1988, 1989 and 1992?

4. Two Bundesliga teams play in Munich, Bayern and which other club?

5. Which Dutch side did Bobby Robson manage after leaving the England manager's post in 1990?

6. Which Serie A side is nicknamed 'Viola' and have won the Italian title on two occasions, in 1956 and 1969?

7. Which Italian side did Liam Brady join on leaving Arsenal in 1980?

8. When Paris St Germain won the French League title for the first time in 1986, which current English Premiership boss was their manager?

9. Which club side provided the majority of the Russian World Cup team of 1986?

10. Which Spanish club has had that serial sacker of football managers, Jesus Gil, as its chairman?

11. Which city's derby matches are played in two different continents, Europe and Asia?

12. Mechelen won the 1988 European Cup Winners Cup final against Ajax, but in which country are they based?

13. In 1966 which was the first German side to win a European trophy, doing so in the Cup Winners Cup final?

14. Lyngby, Aarhus and Brondby have all been league champions in which European country?

15. Which legendary German forward of the 1960s, who played in the 1966 World Cup final, scored a club record 137 league goals for Hamburg during his career?

WORLD INTERNATIONALS

1. Who was the Frenchman sent-off in the 1998 World Cup Final?

2. Which previous Italian national manager succeeded Sven Goran Eriksson at Lazio?

3. Which country has appeared in five European Championship Finals?

4. Apart from England which other country has been managed by Terry Venables?

5. For which African country does the former World Player of the Year George Weah play international football?

6. Hossam Hassan became the world's most capped footballer in 2001 when he won his 151st cap, but for which country does he play?

7. Which country was voted the best African side of the century in 2001?

8. Who was the Everton player involved in the incident that saw Laurent Blanc of France sent-off in the 1998 World Cup semi-final?

9. What unique, but unwanted, feat was achieved by Martin Palermo of Argentina in a Copa America game against Colombia in 1999?

10. Which is the only country to appear in all 16 World Cup finals tournaments?

11. Which famous international player was nicknamed 'The Galloping Major'?

12. Whose first appearance at Old Trafford after joining Manchester United in 1991 was in a Rous Cup match between Russia and Argentina ?

13. Which country has won two of three Women's World Cup finals, in 1991 and on home territory in 1999?

14. What nickname is given to the Nigerian international side?

15. Who scored for Brazil in the World Cup Final in 1958 and 1962, the first player to score in two finals?

BEST OF BRITISH

1. Who left the Welsh manager's post after failing to qualify for the 1994 World Cup finals in the USA?

2. Now manager of Hibernian, who won 77 caps for Scotland from 1980 to 1993?

3. Which current player has won over 50 caps for Northern Ireland whilst with Wimbledon, West Ham and Manchester City amongst others?

4. While at which club did Gary Speed win his first cap for Wales in May 1990 against Costa Rica?

5. Against which country did Scotland clinch qualification for the 1978 World Cup Finals with a 2–0 win at Anfield?

6. Who did Sammy McIlroy replace as the manager of Northern Ireland in 2000?

7. Wales recorded their last victory against England at Wembley in 1977 when which former Burnley and Leeds player scored from the penalty spot?

8. Which midfielder won 76 caps for Scotland from 1984–97 whilst with Celtic to become the Glasgow club's most capped player?

9. In the 1982 World Cup Northern Ireland opened the tournament with a 0–0 draw with which country?

10. Which country beat Wales 2–1 at the Cardiff Arms Park in 1993 to prevent Wales from qualifying for the Finals?

11. Which Rangers player crucial spot-kick against Wales in 1985 enabled Scotland to qualify for a play-off spot for the 1986 finals?

12. Which central defender won 91 caps for Northern Ireland from 1980–1994 to become the country's most capped outfield player?

13. Ian Rush was capped for Wales in the 1980s whilst with Juventus, but which Welshman also did this in the 1950s?

14. During the 1980s who became the first Scotsman capped for his country whilst playing for a Spanish club?

15. Northern Ireland's last win at Wembley was in 1972, who was their player-manager who scored the only goal of the game?

QUICKFIRE

1. In 1999 which forward became the second most expensive English player in history when being transferred for £10million?

2. Managed by Mark Wright in 2000–1, which current non-league side won the old Fourth Division title in 1972–3?

3. For which forward did Liverpool pay a British record fee of £2.9million in 1991?

4. Which Cameroon and West Ham player had the unenviable distinction of having been sent off in two successive World Cups?

5. When Arsenal did 'the Double' in 1971 and 1998, which English side won the European Cup Winners Cup in the same years?

6. Alphabetically which is the last club in the Football League?

7. Which player between 1956–1974 played in a record 713 league games for Southampton?

8. Who played for Oldham in the 1990 League Cup Final and Tranmere Rovers in that final ten years later?

9. Which London club's only two seasons in top flight football were in seasons 1988–89 and 1989–90?

10. Who scored Poland's goal in the 1–1 draw in 1973 which effectively sent England out of the World Cup – at Wembley?

11. Which was the only country in Euro 2000 to fail to gain a point in the group stages?

12. Who played for Marseille in the 1999 UEFA Cup final before joining Liverpool in the summer of that year?

13. When Bobby Charlton appeared in the 1956 FA Youth Cup final against Chesterfield which future World Cup winning team-mate was playing for the opposition?

14. Which Turkish side did Graeme Souness manage?

15. Which English club side defeated Anderlecht 10–0 in a European Cup match in 1956–57?

QUICKFIRE

1. Who in May 1997 became the youngest Premiership goalscorer at 17 years five months?

2. Who has scored a Premiership hat trick with QPR, Newcastle and Spurs?

3. Which club in 1997 were docked two points for refusing to play Blackburn Rovers because they had so many injured players?

4. Who scored England's first goal in Euro 2000 after only three minutes against Portugal?

5. Who was the first foreigner to score in both the FA and Football League Cup finals at Wembley?

6. For which player did Stockport receive their record transfer fee from Middlesbrough of £1.6million in February 1998?

7. Which club won the Premiership in 1995, their first top-flight success in 81 years?

8. Name the brothers who played in losing FA Cup semi-finals in 1997 and 1998 with Wimbledon and Sheffield United respectively?

9. Who is Oldham's most capped international with 24 caps for Norway?

10. In Euro 2000 which country had a player sent off in all three group matches?

11. For which club did current Swansea manager John Hollins once play in an FA Cup final?

12. Who in 1993 became Plymouth's oldest player and the following year saw his son become the youngest player?

13. Which player won promotion with Crystal Palace, Oldham, and Barnsley but lost in the 2000 play-off with Wigan?

14. In September 1977 who became the first knight to become a league manager when joining Birmingham City?

15. On 16 September 1967 George Graham got married on the morning of the North London derby. His best-man played against him in the afternoon – who was it?

The Group phase

1. Prior to Roy Keane in 2000 the previous five winners of the Football Writers' Player of the Year award had all been born outside the British Isles, who were they?
   (5 points)

2. Liverpool won the FA Cup three times from 1986–92, which three players appeared in all three finals?
   (3 points)

3. Since the Premiership started in the 1992–93 season, which four clubs have been relegated from the top flight to Division One on two or more occasions to the end of the 1999–2000 season?
   (4 points)

Penalty Shoot-out

1. Which England international scored for Everton in an FA Cup final during the 1980s?

2. Which Republic of Ireland player scored the first goal conceded by England in the 1990 World Cup?

3. Which club has won Serie A on a record 25 occasions?

4. In February 1999 who became the first substitute to score four times in a Premiership game?

5. Who was the first club to achieve the FA Cup and League Championship double in the Twentieth Century?

Full-time

The most number of appearances in the top ten of the voting for the European Footballer of the Year is the eleven made by Franz Beckenbauer in consecutive years from 1966–76. Johan Cruyff finished in the top ten of the voting on nine occasions.

TV pundit – who shall remain nameless – after the Spain v Yugoslavia game in Euro 2000: 'Hierro was magnificent for the Spaniards tonight.' One problem . . . he wasn't playing.

East Fife are the only side to have won the Scottish Cup whilst in the second division. Prior to 1993 they had also been the only Second Division side to win the League Cup.

The Group phase

1. Which four clubs have won the French title on seven or more occasions?
   (4 points)

2. Since 1990 five clubs have joined the Football League for the first time in their history, who are they?
   (5 points)

3. England have been involved in four penalty shoot-outs in major championships, which three players have taken penalties in three of them?
   (3 points)

Penalty Shoot-out

1. In 1999 who was the last substitute to score in an FA Cup final at Wembley?

2. Which Liverpool player scored on his England debut against Greece in 1982?

3. Which Nationwide Division One manager scored four times for Birmingham City in a league match in 1970 aged just 16?

4. Which club has been in the top flight of English football every season since the end of World War II?

5. Which Manchester United player was the first teenager to appear for England in eight years against the Republic of Ireland in 1991?

Full-time

Question: which group had number one hits in 1970 and 1990 with their only other chart success being in 1982?

Answer: the England World Cup squad.

It's rumoured that on at least one of those records sound engineers unplugged the microphones of several players – whose voices were not up to scratch – without telling them.

Tannoy announcer at the Bristol derby: 'Here comes the Bristol City substitute Junior Bent. I bet he is.' He was promptly sacked. In 1995 the Swindon announcer was sacked for saying at half-time over the PA: 'I've seen some crap refereeing decisions, but that's the worst'.

Burma is reported to have 1,840 referees, but only 1,231 players. In 1966 Workington had 13 directors and only 12 players

BRITISH CLUBS

1. For which Crewe player did Derby County pay £3 million in May 1999?

2. Who are the 'Robins' who play at Ashton Gate?

3. Which North West band partnered England to the top of the charts in 1990 with 'World in Motion'?

4. Who in September 1997 became the first player to score the top three goals in the BBC TV Goal Of The Month competition?

5. For which North West club did Graeme Jones, the leading league goalscorer in 1996–97, play that season?

6. Who scored a record 148 league goals in his three spells at Watford?

7. Which legendary figure managed Hartlepool from 1965–1967?

8. What football innovation was introduced in the disastrous winter of 1963 and is still with us today?

9. Which football manager was the star of the 1994 documentary *An Impossible Job*?

10. Which club were runners-up in the Championship in both 1980–1 and 1981–82?

11. Which full-back joined Everton from Blackburn in July 1979 and played in the 1984 FA Cup final?

12. Which player appeared in FA Cup semi-finals at Wembley in 1994 for Manchester United and 2000 for Aston Villa?

13. Which Italian player captained his country when his father was the manager?

14. In Ruud Gullit's first game in charge of Newcastle who scored a first half hat-trick for Liverpool?

15. Which future Premier League player scored Sweden's winning goal against England in the 1992 European Championships?

BRITISH CLUBS

1. Who are the Clarets who play at Turf Moor?

2. Who partnered Glenn Hoddle to chart success with "Diamond Lights" in 1987?

3. For which striker did Tottenham pay Crystal Palace £4.5million in June 1995?

4. Now a TV pundit, he was voted both the PFA and Young Player Of The Year in 1977 – who is he?

5. In the 1980s which club won the FA Cup just 11 years after joining the League?

6. Graham Moseley once conceded six goals in an FA Cup final and replay – which club was he with?

7. Richard Dinnis, Gordon Lee and Bill McGarry all managed which current Premiership club in 1977?

8. Although born in England, he played twice in goal for Scotland in 1971 and is now a TV presenter. Who is he?

9. Which current Premiership manager played in the 1958 World Cup for England ?

10. Which club won the Football League in their first season in the top flight in 1961–2?

11. Which club won the First Division with a record 127 goals in 1930–1?

12. Against Holland in 1988, who became the last player to score at both ends in an international for England?

13. Which 1978 World Cup winner for Argentina played for Valencia in the 1980 Cup Winners Cup final against Arsenal?

14. Which Aston Villa player in 1994 had been the last player to score from the spot in a League Cup final prior to 2001?

15. Who were the cousins, with the same surname, who were both included in 1998 England's World Cup squad?

NEWCASTLE UNITED

1. Which player set a club record with 41 goals in the 1993–4 season?

2. Which former Liverpool player was the top scorer in the 1997–8 season with six goals in the Premiership?

3. Which Republic of Ireland international was the NewcastleUnited goalkeeper in the 1998 FA Cup final?

4. Who in July 1996 joined the Geordies for a club record £15million?

5. Now with Everton this defender was Newcastle's youngest player in 1990 aged 16 years 223 day. Who is he?

6. Which World Cup winner in 1978 managed the club in 1991–2?

7. Who was voted French Player Of The Year in 1994 and moved to Tyneside in the summer of 1995?

8. Against which club did Alan Shearer score five times in a league match in September 1999?

9. Who was the first German international to appear in a FA Cup final?

10. Who was the first Brazilian international to play in league football?

11. Which club did United defeat to win the Fairs Cup in 1969?

12. Which legendary player scored a record 200 goals for the club 1946–57?

13. In 1988 Newcastle bought Andy Thorn and Dave Beasant, both for £850,000, from which club?

14. Who were the brothers who appeared together in the Newcastle side which won the FA Cup final in 1952?

15. Which World Cup winner of 1966 later managed the Tyneside club?

SUNDERLAND

1.   Who scored the goal that knocked Sunderland out of the
     FA Cup in 2000–1?

2.   Sunderland now play at the Stadium of Light – where did
     they play prior to the move?

3.   From which league club did Sunderland sign Kevin
     Phillips?

4.   Name the current Sunderland player who played for
     Arsenal before moving to Fiorentina and Valencia?

5.   Now an ITV pundit, in the 1985 League Cup final he
     became the youngest man to captain any final side at
     Wembley?

6.   Which club defeated Sunderland the last time they reached
     the FA Cup Final?

7.   Who scored an own goal in the 1985 League Cup Final
     against Norwich City?

8.   Who played for Newcastle when they won the FA Cup in
     1955 and later managed Sunderland to FA Cup Final
     success?

9.   Which former England international centre-half became
     manager of the club in 1993?

10. Who in 1999 became the first Sunderland player to appear
     for England at the Stadium of Light?

11. And prior to 1999, who in 1976 was the last Sunderland
     player to win a full England cap at Wembley?

12. Who travelled to Euro 2000 as understudy to Peter
     Schmeichel for his country?

13. Which Sunderland legend is the club's most capped player
     with 38 Republic of Ireland Caps?

14. Which member of the 1973 FA Cup winning team played
     for Manchester City in the 1981 final?

15. Which Sunderland player was signed from St. Johnstone
     in 1981 for £350,000, then the most expensive fee for an
     18–year-old in British football?

FA CUP – THE 1970s

1. Who managed a side in the final for the only time when taking charge of Liverpool against Manchester United in 1977?

2. And in the same final who is officially credited with scoring United's winning goal after a Lou Macari shot struck him before going in?

3. Who was the Southampton manager when they won the trophy for the first time in 1976?

4. Who captained Leeds United in all three of their finals during the decade?

5. Whose spectacular shot, from outside the box, gave Arsenal the Cup in 1971 against Liverpool?

6. Which forward was on the losing side twice during the decade, for Newcastle in 1974 and Arsenal in 1978?

7. In which year of the decade did the famous 'five minute final' take place when three goals were scored in the last five minutes?

8. Which future Ipswich Town manager played for the club when they won the Cup in 1978?

9. Which Third Division side, inspired by future England coach Peter Taylor, reached the semi-finals in 1976 before losing to Southampton?

10. When West Ham United played Fulham in 1975 it was only the second all-London final. Who played for Fulham in that game and for Spurs in the first one against Chelsea in 1967?

11. Liverpool reached the 1971 and 1977 finals after beating which side in both semi-finals?

12. Who played for Sunderland in the 1973 final and later won 65 caps for England at centre-half?

13. Which side did Arsenal beat in the semi-finals of both 1971 and 1972, both matches going to replays?

14. Which non-league side famously took Leeds United to a replay at Selhurst Park in the fourth round in 1975?

15. Which current Premiership club's only semi-final appearance of the decade was when losing 3–1 to Liverpool in a replay in 1974?

THE LEAGUE CUP

1. Which club has won the League Cup on a record six occasions?

2. Which club did Birmingham City beat on aggregate in the semi-final of the competition in 2000–1?

3. Who was the manager of Chelsea when they won the trophy in 1998?

4. Who scored for Manchester United in the 1983 final aged 17?

5. Who managed two different teams that beat Manchester United in the final in the 1990s?

6. In which year was there an all-Merseyside final in the competition?

7. Which member of England's 1966 World Cup winning side set a record by scoring 49 times in the competition?

8. Which player won winner's medals with both Nottingham Forest in 1978 and Arsenal in 1987?

9. Which First Division side reached the final of the competition for the first time in 1999–2000?

10. Who scored in the 1996 European Cup final and then in the 1997 League Cup final for Middlesbrough?

11. Who scored both Tottenham's goals when they beat Aston Villa 2–0 in the final in 1971?

12. Which club reached the final for the only time in their history in 1985 against Norwich?

13. Who was sent-off in the 1994 final for Manchester United after handling a goal bound shot on the line?

14. Which ground staged the 1997 replay between Leicester City and Middlesbrough?

15. Which club won a major trophy for the first time in their history when beating QPR 3–0 in the 1986 final?

EUROPEAN CHAMPIONS CUP

1. Apart from Roy Keane, which other Manchester United was suspended for the 1999 European Cup final?

2. Who was the goalkeeper who was an unused substitute for Manchester United in the 1968 final and had to be replaced shortly after the start of the 1982 final when playing for Aston Villa?

3. How many times have Real Madrid won the trophy?

4. Who was the charismatic manager of Nottingham Forest when they won the trophy twice?

5. Which side scored four times in the finals of 1969, 1989 and 1994?

6. In 1974 which club became the only side to win the competition after a replay?

7. In 1997–98 which country became the first to field three teams in the European Champions Cup?

8. Which English international played for Hamburg against Nottingham Forest in the 1980 final?

9. Who scored a famous winning goal for Leeds when they beat Lazio in Rome in the second stage of the Champion League in 2000–1?

10. Who scored for Liverpool in the final of the competition in both 1977 and 1984, the only Englishman to achieve this feat?

11. Which English side lost their first ever home match in Europe in a Champions Cup group game against Lazio in March 2000?

12. Who during the 1980s was the last Englishman to manage a team in the final?

13. Who were Celtic's opponents when a competition record of 135,826 saw a European Cup semi-final at Hampden Park in 1970?

14. And at Hampden Park in 1960 which side were beaten 7–3 by Real Madrid in the highest scoring final?

15. Which defender surprisingly scored two late goals to enable Arsenal to defeat Shaktar Donetsk at Highbury by 3–2 in the 2000–1 competition?

EUROPEAN CLUBS – General

1. Which country recorded its only major European trophy success when Ferencvaros defeated Juventus 1–0 in the 1965 UEFA Cup final?

2. Which European club finished in third place in the FIFA World Club Championship in 2000?

3. Which player scored six times for Barcelona in the opening group phase of the 2000–1 Champions Cup, even though they failed to progress into the next stage?

4. Which manager, with 28 major trophies, had won more trophies than any other man in European football at the start of the 2000–1 season?

5. Later to manage Celtic to the Scottish title, he appeared in the Feyenoord side who defeated the Glasgow club in the 1970 European Champions Cup final?

6. What is the name of the trophy played between the winners of the UEFA Cup and European Champions Cup?

7. Which Spanish club did Claudio Ranieri coach before he joined Chelsea?

8. Which European Cup winning side is known as 'Crvena Zvezda' in their own country?

9. Which Dutch international moved from PSV Eindhoven to Barcelona for £5 million in 1989?

10. Which is the only British club to have played more than 200 games in European competitions?

11. Which QPR player was the leading goalscorer in the 1976–77 UEFA Cup with 11 goals?

12. Which then European country, which is no longer in existence, won their only European trophy when FC Magdeburg won the Cup Winners Cup in 1974?

13. Which famous winger was the only member of the great Real Madrid side of the late 1950s to play against Chelsea for Real Madrid in the 1971 Cup Winners Cup final?

14. Which Italian club plays at the Sao Paolo stadium?

15. Regarded as the greatest Polish player of all time, he scored the winner for Juventus in the 1984 Cup Winners Cup final and was part of the team that won the European Cup a year later – who is he?

ENGLAND

1. Which player scored for England after just 27 seconds against France in the 1982 World Cup?

2. Which Manchester United defender made his England debut after just 11 first team appearances against Hungary in 1999?

3. Against Sweden in 1999 who became the first Englishman sent-off in a full international at Wembley?

4. Who scored four times for England, as well as missing a penalty, in the 6–0 win over San Marino at Wembley in 1993?

5. Which club side provided seven players when England played France at Wembley in February 1999?

6. Which two players, with the same name, were included in England's 1986 World Cup squad?

7. Which member of England's 1966 World Cup winning side scored 18 goals in his 34 internationals?

8. Who played for England in three decades – the 1950s, 60s and 70s?

9. Which country deprived England of a place in the 1978 World Cup Finals by finishing above them in the qualifying group?

10. In the 1996–97 season who was capped for England whilst a player-manager in the Premiership?

11. Who scored the only goal when Italy beat England 1–0 in their World Cup qualifying match at Wembley in 1997?

12. Besides David Batty, who missed a penalty for England in the shootout against Argentina in France 98?

13. In 1968 against Yugoslavia who was the first Englishman sent-off in a full international?

14. Against which country did Alan Shearer score his first and only England hat-trick in September 1999?

15. Two England managers also managed Fulham during their career – Kevin Keegan was one but who was the other?

REPUBLIC OF IRELAND

1. Who is the only man to manage the Republic in the World Cup finals?

2. Who scored the only goal for the Republic when they beat England 1–0 in the 1988 European Championships?

3. Who played for Leeds in the Premiership in 2000–1 and in 1998 against Malta became the youngest-ever player to score for the Republic?

4. Which forward with 88 caps is the Republic's most capped player?

5. Which country beat the Republic on away goals to qualify for the finals of Euro 2000?

6. Who won 72 caps for the Republic between 1974 and 1990 whilst with four Italian clubs amongst others?

7. Who when playing for the Republic in 1991 became the first Tranmere Rovers player to win an international cap since 1959?

8. Which current player has won caps for the Republic whilst with Bolton, Liverpool and Blackburn Rovers?

9. Which long serving centre-half was capped 71 times between 1980 and 1994 whilst with Manchester United, Sporting Gijon and Blackburn Rovers?

10. Which then-Portsmouth player's goal at Windsor Park in 1993 in a 1–1 draw enabled the Republic to qualify for the World Cup finals?

11. Which Premiership club provided four players in the Republic's famous win over Italy in the 1994 World Cup finals?

12. Who was player-manager of the Republic between 1976 and 1980?

13. Which QPR player scored 4 times for the Republic when they beat Turkey 4–0 in Dublin in October 1975?

14. Who made his Republic of Ireland debut against Chile in May 1991 whilst with Nottingham Forest?

15. Which country has beaten the Republic in the final stages of both the World Cup and European Championships?

QUICKFIRE

1. Who was the first manager from outside Britain to win the then-First Division-Premiership title?

2. Which player appeared in an FA Cup winning side in three decades – 1988, 1997 and 2000?

3. Who was the player who made 61 England appearances – 56 with Liverpool and five with Tottenham?

4. Which club side did Graham Taylor leave to become England manager in 1990?

5. Who scored a record 12 goals for Tottenham in the 1986–7 Football League Cup campaign?

6. Who was the last Welshman to captain the FA Cup winners at Wembley?

7. Which Liverpool player was both the PFA and Football Writers' Player Of The Year in 1980?

8. Which North West club was the first club to win all four divisions of the Football League?

9. Which goalkeeper won Championship medals with Everton in 1987 and Blackburn in 1995?

10. Who played for Wealdstone and Coventry City in the early 1980s before winning England caps later in his career?

11. How did Rotherham make FA Cup history in 1991?

12. Two unrelated Welsh forwards, Ron and Wyn, played for Manchester United in the 1970s – but what was their surname?

13. Who scored the winning goal in the all-Sheffield FA Cup semi-final at Wembley in 1993?

14. Who played his first game for England in 1935 and his last 22 years later?

15. Which club in 1992 had to resign from the league due to debt problems?

QUICKFIRE

1. Which overseas goalkeeper won three FA Cup winner's medals, all in the 1990s?

2. Prior to 2001 who was the last Englishman to score in a European Champions Cup final?

3. Against which club did David Beckham score from the halfway line on the opening day of the 1996–7 season?

4. Which club in 1997 became only the seventh side from the Third Division to reach the FA Cup semi-finals?

5. Who began the 1998–9 season with Crystal Palace yet ended up with a European Cup Winners Cup medal?

6. Which club in 1968–9 suffered only two defeats in the First Division?

7. Which club went a record 42 league games unbeaten from November 1977 to December 1978?

8. Which current Premiership club were runners-up to Liverpool in 1983–84, their best-ever league finish?

9. In the 2000–1 season who played against Aston Villa for both Sunderland and Ipswich Town in the space of a week?

10. Which manager saw his side score the winning goal in a FA Cup quarter-final tie in 2000–1 from inside the tunnel after being earlier being sent from the touchline?

11. What was Brighton's home ground until they left in 1997?

12. Which current Spurs player is in the top six all-time leading goalscorers in the European Cup?

13. Who kept goal for West Germany in their 1974 World Cup-winning side?

14. Who was the Nottingham Forest player who scored the winning penalty in the 1978 League Cup final?

15. Who between 1978 and 1986 managed the Midlands 'big three' of Aston Villa, West Brom and Birmingham City?

The Group phase

1. Against which four countries did Gary Lineker score hat-
    tricks for England?
    (4 points)

2. Which three clubs were promoted to the Premiership for
    the 1999–2000 season?
    (3 points)

3. Who are the five British players to have been voted
    European Footballer of the Year?
    (5 points)

Penalty Shoot-out

1. Who top-scored for Arsenal when they won the
    Premiership in 1997–98?

2. In 1989 who became the first Wimbledon player to be
    capped by England?

3. Which club did Manchester United defeat by a single goal
    to win the Toyota Cup in 1999 to become World Club
    Champions?

4. In 1970 who became the first player to move between
    English clubs for £200,000 when leaving West Ham for
    Spurs?

5. Who was the legendary Wolves manager of the 1950s who
    sadly died in 2001?

Full-time

In the third round of the FA Cup, in three consecutive seasons from 1955–56 to 1957–58, Cardiff City were drawn away to Leeds United at Elland Road. They won all three matches by 2–1.

Des Lynam on the 'Goal of the World Cup' competition: 'This is what you do: Pick a player, call 0898–991199 . . . and if a girl called Mandy answers, you've got the wrong number.'

The 1982 World Cup final was the first to start on time since 1970. In 1978 the final was delayed when Argentina protested over the dressing on Dutchman Rene van de Kerkhof's arm. The 1974 final was delayed when it was noticed that, in the most important match on the planet, officials had forgotten to put corner flags on the pitch.

The Group phase

1. Sir Alex Ferguson has managed which four clubs during his career?
   (4 points)

2. Which three players had been sold by English to Spanish clubs for more than £10 million, prior to Emmanuel Petit and Marc Overmars moving to Barcelona in 2000?
   (3 points)

3. Prior to the 2000–1 season, who are the five different clubs to be runners-up in the Premiership since it started in 1992–93?
   (5 points)

Penalty Shoot-out

1. Which current Premiership manager ended his 20–year association with Arsenal after winning the FA Cup in 1993?

2. On which Premiership ground did Scotland play both Holland and Switzerland in Euro 96?

3. Which England manager left his position in the 1970s to take a job in the desert?

4. For which club did the Brazilians Falcao and Cerezo play against Liverpool in the European Cup final?

5. From which Scottish club was Duncan Ferguson sold to Rangers for a British record fee of £4 million in July 1993?

Full-time

Luis Monti can uniquely claim to have appeared for two countries in the World Cup final, for the losers Argentina in 1930 and Italy when they won in 1934.

When current Everton manager Walter Smith and his renowned 'hard-man' coach Archie Knox were involved in the Scottish national squad, they played a friendly game against the Scottish wheelchair soccer team. Halfway through a hard-fought match Knox was thrown to the ground from his chair following a hard tackle. At the end of the game, in which they were badly beaten, Knox complained, 'That wheelchair soccer is tough, I could hardly move in the second half.'

At this point one of his opponents confessed: 'Don't tell Archie, but when he wasn't looking after that tackle I stuck the handbrake on on his wheelchair'.

When Graeme Souness scored the winning goal for Spurs in the 1970 Youth Cup final against Coventry City, the opposition goalkeeper was future BBC presenter and self-proclaimed prophet David Icke.

BRITISH CLUBS

1.   What nationality is Leeds United's Lucas Radebe?

2.   Which current Liverpool player scored on his League, FA Cup, League Cup and European debuts for the club?

3.   Which former Wimbledon striker is a part-time model and played for Bolton in the 2000–1 season?

4.   Who was described as the 'new Robbie Keane' when moving to Coventry City for a fee of £6.5 million in the summer of 2000?

5.   For which club did Gary Lineker, Alan Smith, and Mark Bright all play in their careers?

6.   Who managed Aberdeen to three Scottish Championships during the 1980s?

7.   In the 1974 Charity Shield who was the first Englishman sent-off at Wembley?

8.   For which player did Leicester City pay Notts County a fee of £1.25 million in 1994 and then sell to Aston Villa for £3.25 million in 1995?

9.   For which club did Alan Hunter win 47 of his 53 Northern Ireland caps?

10. Who scored five goals for Gillingham against Burnley in 1998–99 having moved from Brentford for £500,000?

11. Which Nigerian international played for Tottenham and Notts County during the 1980s?

12. Which club joined the League in 1977 and had their record defeat of 8–0 against Everton in the League Cup 12 months later?

13. Which side scored four goals in just four minutes 44 seconds of a Premiership game against Southampton in 1993?

14. Which Norwich City player scored just 13 seconds after coming on as a substitute in December 1994 against Chelsea?

15. Which club in 1992–93 knocked Crystal Palace out of the FA Cup and then went on a run of 13 league and cup matches without scoring a goal?

BRITISH CLUBS

1. Dens Park is the ground of which Scottish club?

2. Which player moved from Wimbledon to Coventy in 2001 on a 'pay-as-you-play' basis?

3. Who are 'the Saddlers' who played at Fellows Park and now play at the Bescot Stadium?

4. Who was the only Liverpool player to appear in both their 1995 and 2001 League Cup successes?

5. Who was in charge of QPR when they were runners-up in the league to Liverpool in 1976 before he moved to Manchester United?

6. Which club received a record fee for Shaka Hislop of £1.5 million in 1995 from Newcastle United?

7. Which club holds the record for the lowest attendance in the Premiership of just over 3,000 fans in 1993?

8. Who returned to Cambridge United as manager in March 2001 as replacement for Roy MacFarland, nine years after being sacked?

9. With which Scottish club did George Best once play?

10. Ian Callaghan played in 88 FA Cup matches for three clubs, Liverpool were one – name either of the others?

11. Which club won the First Division title in 1995–96 and 1998–99?

12. Which club in 1996–97 scored a Premiership record of just 28 goals in the season?

13. Which club won the Scottish title for the only time in 1962 with Alan Gilzean and Ian Ure in the side?

14. Which veteran goalkeeper came on as a substitute for Manchester City against Newcastle in 1995 aged 43 years?

15. Which club was relegated following their only season in the Premiership in 1993–94 when they conceded over 100 goals?

CELTIC

1. Which former Liverpool player was appointed head coach of the club in the summer of 1999?

2. Who was the clubs leading scorer in the league with 25 goals in the 1999–2000 season before joining Leeds United?

3. Which player moved to Celtic from Leicester City in the 2000–1 season?

4. Which player scored over 100 league goals for Celtic during the 1970s before matching that feat in England?

5. Which Scottish captain moved to Monaco from Celtic under a 'Bosman' transfer?

6. Who won a PFA Player of the Year award with Arsenal in 1979 and would later manage Celtic?

7. Which former Celtic goalkeeper won 80 caps for the Republic of Ireland?

8. Which current international manager won a Scottish League winner's medal with Celtic in 1988?

9. Which controversial striker moved from Celtic to Nottingham Forest in 1997?

10. Which English club knocked Celtic out of the UEFA Cup on away goals in the 1997–98 competition?

11. Which defender played over 650 times for Celtic, and won 62 Scottish caps whilst at the club in a career that stretched from 1967 to 1987?

12. Who scored 397 league goals for Celtic in a career from 1922 to 1938, the highest with a Scottish club?

13. Which player moved from Celtic to Sheffield Wednesday for a fee of £4.7 million in August 1997?

14. Which Celtic player was sent-off in the 1984 Scottish FA Cup final?

15. Who kept goal for Celtic in the 1967 European Cup final 12 years after winning a FA Cup winner's medal with Newcastle United?

RANGERS

1. Which TV pundit holds the record for scoring the most goals in a career for Rangers?

2. Who managed the club to the Scottish league title in 1999–2000?

3. In 1986 who became the first player-manager in the club's history, having previously won many honours with Liverpool?

4. Which man has represented Scotland at both cricket and football and moved to Rangers from Hibernian in 1991 for a record fee for his position?

5. Which player has won League Championship medals with both Rangers and Leeds United?

6. Which player has uniquely scored in a Manchester, Merseyside and Glasgow derby, doing so in the latter for Rangers in March 2000?

7. Which England international was sold to Marseille in 1991 for £5.5 million?

8. Which side did Rangers beat 4–0 in the Scottish Cup final in 2000?

9. Which player scored five times in a SPL game for Rangers against Dundee United in 1997?

10. Who in 1995 became the first overseas player to win the Scottish Writers Player of the Year award?

11. Who played for Rangers when they won the Scottish Cup in 1973 before uniquely winning the trophy with Celtic in 1977?

12. Which player scored for Rangers in the 1990 League Cup defeat of Celtic before moving to Liverpool in 1991?

13. Which Rangers legend played a record 496 league games for the club from 1962 to 1978, mainly in defence?

14. From which club did Rangers sign the late, great Jim Baxter?

15. Who left the club in the late 1980s to become player manager of QPR?

FA CUP – THE 1990s

1. Which club won the FA Cup on most occasions during the decade?

2. Who scored the only goal of the final in 1996?

3. In which year did Wembley stage an FA Cup semi-final for the first time?

4. Which Second Division side took Middlesbrough to a replayed semi-final in 1997?

5. In 1993 who was the first American to appear in the final –doing so for Sheffield Wednesday?

6. Which non-league side took Newcastle to a replay at St James Park in 1997–98 before losing 2–1?

7. Who played for Manchester United and Chelsea in finals during the decade?

8. Which side were originally barred from the competition in 1994–95 but reached the semi-finals after being reinstated?

9. Who was the manager of Sunderland in the 1992 final?

10. Which side inflicted Man Uniteds only defeat at Old Trafford in the FA Cup during the decade – on penalties in 1992 after a 2–2 draw?

11. Which side beat Liverpool 4–3 in an FA Cup semi-final during the decade after losing 9–0 in a League match at Anfield earlier in the season?

12. Which player scored for Newcastle in the 1998 and 1999 FA Cup semi-finals?

13. Which TV commentator covered his last FA Cup final in 1998 before retiring?

14. Who managed a side against Man United in two semi-finals and an FA Cup final during the decade?

15. Who scored a his only hat-trick in his two seasons for Liverpool in their 7–0 home victory against Rochdale in the third round in 1996?

THE SCOTTISH CUPS

1. Which club has won the Scottish Cup on most occasions?
2. Which club won the Scottish Cup in 1998 by beating Rangers 2–1 to record their first victory in the final since 1956?
3. Who won an FA Cup winner's medal with Manchester United in 1994 and two Scottish Cup winner's medals with Rangers in 1999 and 2000?
4. When Celtic recorded their only Scottish Cup Final victory of the 1990s – in 1995 – which controversial Dutch striker scored the only goal of the game?
5. Which England international striker scored for Rangers in the Scottish Cup finals of 1992 and 1993?
6. Which future Derby County player scored for Celtic in their 3–0 League Cup final victory over Dundee United in November 1997?
7. Which player scored for Arsenal in the 1987 League Cup final and for Celtic in the 1994 Scottish League Cup final?
8. Which club won the Scottish Cup final by defeating Rangers 1–0 in 1994 after losing all of their previous five finals in the preceding 13 years?
9. Who is the only man to manage FA Cup winning sides both North and South of the border?
10. Who was the acting manager of Celtic when they won the Scottish League Cup final in March 2000?
11. Which veteran goalkeeper was playing his last game for Aberdeen in the 2000 Scottish Cup final but was substituted after eight minutes through injury?
12. Who scored a hat-trick for Rangers when they beat Celtic 3–2 in the Scottish League Cup final in March 1984?
13. Which club was beaten 6–1 by Celtic in the 1972 Scottish Cup final and 6–3, by the same side, in the Scottish League Cup final in October 1974?
14. Which club shocked Celtic by winning the Scottish League final on penalties in November 1994 after a 2–2 draw?
15. Who captained Spurs in an English FA Cup final in the 1980s and Rangers in a Scottish Cup final in the 1990s?

EUROPEAN CUP WINNERS CUP

1. Who scored both Manchester United's goals in their final victory against Barcelona of 1991?

2. Which current Coventry player scored Arsenal's goal in the 1995 final against Real Zaragoza?

3. Which current Premiership player appeared as a substitute for Ajax, aged just 18, in the final of the competition in 1987?

4. Who scored the only goal, after coming on as a substitute, for Chelsea in the 1998 final against Stuttgart?

5. Wembley was the venue for the final in 1993 when which Italian side won their first ever European competition for the first time?

6. Which English side won their only European trophy at Wembley in the 1965 final?

7. Who was the only player to appear for Manchester United in the 1991 Cup Winners Cup final and 1999 European Cup final?

8. Which member of Arsenal's 1998 Double winning side played under Arsene Wenger for Monaco in the 1992 final against Werder Bremen?

9. Everton won the trophy in 1985 but which English international scored their second goal against Rapid Vienna in a 3–1 victory?

10. Who is the only man to manage two different British clubs to victory in the final of the competition?

11. Which Russian club won the final of the competition in both 1975 and 1986?

12. Who was the Leeds 'hard-man' sent off in the 1973 final against AC Milan?

13. Which Spanish side reached their first-ever European final but lost 2–1 to Lazio in 1999?

14. Which player won winners' medals with Real Zaragoza in 1995 and Chelsea in 1998?

15. Who scored the only goal of the 1969 FA Cup final for Man City and opened the scoring when they won the Cup Winners Cup against Gornik Zabrze twelve months later?

THE UEFA CUP

1. Which English side reached the semi-finals of the competition in 1999–2000 after beating Roma in an earlier round?

2. Who scored his first Arsenal hat-trick against Werder Bremen in the 1999–2000 UEFA Cup?

3. What was the UEFA Cup known as between 1958–71?

4. And during this period which English side appeared in the final on three occasions?

5. Who was the manager of Ipswich when they won the competition in 1980–81?

6. Manchester United went out of the competition on away goals in 1995–96 to Rotor Volgograd, but whose equaliser at Old Trafford was his only goal for the club?

7. Who was the Englishman who managed Inter Milan when they lost to Schalke 04 in the 1997 Final?

8. In which country were 1978 losing finalists Bastia based?

9. Which player scored for Arsenal in the 1970 final and later scored for Liverpool in the 1976 Final?

10. Which English side controversially lost 3–2 on aggregate to Anderlecht in the 1984 semi-finals?

11. Later to play for Sheffield Wednesday, this Dutchman scored for Ajax when they won the tournament in 1992 and for Inter Milan when they were victorious in 1994?

12. Which English club, now outside the Premiership, scored 39 goals in just 12 matches in the competition in their only two seasons in Europe in 1976–77 and 1984–85?

13. Which French club knocked Celtic out of the competition in 2000–01?

14. Who scored four goals for Liverpool in the Finals of the UEFA Cup in 1973 and 1976?

15. Which 2000–1 Premiership side have played just one season in Europe, losing 8–2 on aggregate to Bayern Munich in the Second Round in 1970–71?

WORLD CUP

1. Which country was beaten in two World Cup Finals in the 1980s?

2. Who captained Argentina to their World Cup victory in 1986?

3. Who became the first Englishman sent-off in the World Cup finals in the 1986 tournament?

4. Who scored a memorable goal for Scotland in their 3–2 win over Holland in the 1978 World Cup?

5. Which player scored for Italy in the World Cup final stages in 1990,1994 and 1998?

6. In the 1994 finals which Bulgarian scored six goals in the tournament to be joint top scorer?

7. Who scored the winning penalty for the Republic of Ireland in the penalty shoot-out against Romania in the 1990 Finals?

8. Who scored for West Germany in the 1974 World Cup Final and the 1982 Final?

9. Which Premiership player scored Jamaica's only goal of the 1998 finals in France?

10. Later to manage in the Premiership he took charge of Switzerland in the 1994 finals?

11. In which year did all four British home countries qualify for the World Cup for the only time?

12. Who captained Brazil in the 1994 and 1998 World Cup Finals and has made more appearances in the final stages than any other of his countrymen?

13. Which country staged the World Cup final stages in 1954?

14. Who were the brothers who appeared for Holland in the 1978 Final against Argentina?

15. Which country did France beat 1–0 in the 1998 World Cup in the first finals match to be decided by a 'golden goal'?

THE AMERICAS

1. Wanderley Luxemburgo was the manager of which South American country until leaving the post in 2000?

2. Who was the 'chain smoking' manager of the victorious 1978 Argentina World Cup side?

3. Which Colombian goalkeeper is famous for his 'Scorpion' kicks?

4. Featuring a trademark beard and long hair which player was a star for the American side in the 1994 World Cup?

5. Who was the charismatic Mexican goalkeeper in the 1994 World Cup who was also registered an outfield player in the tournament?

6. In which year did the USA record their infamous 1–0 win over England in a World Cup tournament?

7. Which South American country in 1993 became the first team ever to beat Brazil in a World Cup qualifying match, on their way to qualifying for the finals for the first time in 40 years?

8. Famous for his trademark free-kicks, who made 92 appearances for Brazil from 1965 and 1978 and was a star player in their 1970 team?

9. He captained Argentina to the 1978 World Cup and is currently the manager of Uruguay – who is he?

10. Which player scored 30 goals in 58 matches for Mexico in his career as well as being a star centre-forward for Real Madrid in the 1980s?

11. Which South American country was the original choice for the 1986 World Cup until a last minute change to Mexico?

12. In December 2000 which midfielder, who enjoys a special relationship with David Beckham, equalled Oscar Ruggeri's record of 98 caps for Argentina?

13. Which forward scored seven goals for Brazil in the 1986 and 1990 World Cups as well as playing in Italy for Napoli?

14. Which South American country faced England in an international for the only time in May 1970 and lost 2–0?

15. Which Caribbean country qualified for the knock-out stages of the 1990 World Cup after finishing second to Brazil in their group, until losing 4–1 to Czechoslovakia?

QUICKFIRE

1. Who scored 49 goals for England in 106 internationals?

2. Which Liverpool player captained Scotland in the 1982 World Cup finals?

3. Who captained England for the first time when they lost 2–0 to the USA in Graham Taylor's reign as manager?

4. Which former Everton and Sunderland star was sacked as Fulham manager in 2000 to make way for Jean Tigana?

5. In the 1986 World Cup finals which country avenged a defeat against England in 1966 by winning the opening group fixture 1–0?

6. Which current First Division club, in 1931, provided the only instance of a side winning the FA Cup and promotion to the top flight in the same season?

7. Who was the Middlesbrough striker who scored a record nine hat-tricks in the 1926–27 season?

8. Who at the age of 30 years decided to retire from football during 2001 just five weeks after leaving Bradford City?

9. Which Manchester United player scored in both games against Panathinaikos in the Champions Cup Second Stage in 2000–1, including a last minute equaliser in Greece?

10. At which London ground in March 2001 did Chelsea record their first away league victory since April 2000?

11. On the opening day of the 1990–91 season which Everton player was fined a weeks wages for a sit-down protest on the pitch at half-time?

12. At which club were TV pundits Barry Venison and Ally McCoist once team-mates?

13. Why were Stirling Albion forced to play their Scottish FA Cup matches on away grounds in 1989–90?

14. When Peter Shilton won his 108th cap against Poland in 1989, whose English record did he equal for appearances?

15. Which Russian did Ipswich Town sign from Dinamo Kiev in 1988–89 to become the first player from his country to play in the League?

QUICKFIRE

1. Who played for Leeds United in the 1996 League Cup final and Liverpool in the 2001 final?

2. Which current Liverpool player scored twice in a match in Euro 2000 against Denmark?

3. In 1958, which legendary player became the youngest ever to win a World Cup winners medal?

4. Who saved a penalty for England against Spain at Villa Park in 2001?

5. Which country drew four consecutive games in the 1990 World Cup finals?

6. Who was the Watford captain who missed the 1984 FA Cup final through suspension?

7. Who scored in both the 1974 European and World Cup finals – the only player to do so in the same year?

8. Which club won the Cup Winners Cup for a record fourth time in 1997?

9. Which country had a player sent-off after just 55 seconds of a World Cup match against Scotland in 1986?

10. Which player made over 600 appearances for Dundee United from 1974–92 as well as appearing in 76 European matches for the club?

11. Which TV pundit was fired by Oxford United as manager when he complained to chairman Robert Maxwell about the sale of Dean Saunders to Derby County?

12. Which manager in the 1988–89 season was banned from coming on to the pitch after hauling off two of his clubs fans for hooliganism?

13. Which FA Cup giant-killers played at Gander Green Lane and were captained by Tony Rains?

14. Who is the President of FIFA?

15. Which player, who was signed via Teletext, scored Wycombe Wanderers winning goal against Leicester City in the FA Cup sixth round in 2001?

The Group phase

1. Which three countries have England played on three or more occasions in the final stages of the World Cup?
    (3 points)

2. Which six English clubs have appeared in a European final on one occasion only?
    (6 points)

3. In 1999 Kevin Campbell became the first player to score hat-tricks in the Premiership with three different clubs, who are they?
    (3 points)

Penalty Shoot-out

1. For which club did John Aldridge score 30 goals in 42 league matches in the Second Division in 1984–5?

2. Who when playing for Leeds against Spurs in August 1992 scored the first ever Premiership hat-trick?

3. Who came on as a substitute for Steve McMahon against Belgium in the 1990 World Cup finals and scored a last minute winner?

4. Who became acting manager of Sheffield Wednesday for the second time in 12 months in February 2001?

5. From which Spanish side did Manchester United sign Quinton Fortune?

Full-time

On 10 September 1983, Simon Garner scored five times for Blackburn against Derby and Tony Caldwell also scored five for Bolton against Walsall. It was the first time for 18 years that two players had scored five goals in a game, on the same day, in the league. Strangely the next instance was only seven weeks later, when Ian Rush scored five for Liverpool against Luton and Tony Woodcock scored five for Arsenal at Villa Park. Woodcock's five goals were the last such instance of a player scoring five goals for the away side in the English top flight.

Charlton manager Lennie Lawrence on his club's lack of opportunities from the spot: 'The last time we got a penalty away from home, Christ was a carpenter.'

Diego Maradona has captained Argentina 16 times in the World Cup finals, which is a record for any country.

The Group phase

1. Which five players have scored 19 or more goals in
    internationals for the Republic of Ireland?
    (5 points)

2. Which four clubs, one each from Scotland, Germany,
    Romania and France, have won the European Cup once
    and also lost in the final on one occasion?
    (4 points)

3. Which three men have managed Aston Villa in the
    Premiership?
    (3 points)

Penalty Shoot-out

1. In 1994 which veteran Cameroon player became the oldest
    man to score in the World Cup finals?

2. With just one minute left who scored Romania's winner
    against England in Euro 2000?

3. Who was the Chelsea striker who scored in seven
    consecutive games in the Premiership in 1993–94?

4. Which soccer 'hardman' was booked after just three
    seconds of the Chelsea-Sheffield United FA Cup tie in
    1992?

5. Which Division One side, in the 2000–1 season, plays at
    Gresty Road?

Full-time

Dave Bassett once kept his Wimbledon players in the dressing room for an hour after a bad display in the old Fourth Division, saying, 'You lot are just a bunch of clowns and amateurs going nowhere'. On the way home the team bus he was driving quickly came to a halt. He'd forgotten to fill it up with petrol.

'The referee is looking at his watch and the crowd is pleading with him to blow it' – anonymous radio commentator.

In the Italian Serie A in 1978–79 Perugia failed to win the title despite remaining unbeaten in their 30 games that season, winning 19 times but drawing on 11 occasions. AC Milan lost three times but still won the title by three points.

BRITISH CLUBS

1.   In June 1999 Liverpool signed which goalkeeper for a record fee of £4million?

2.   After winning 88 caps for Northern Ireland, he later became manager of Macclesfield Town – who is he?

3.   Who in 1995–6 season scored five Premiership hat tricks?

4.   Which former Nottingham Forest player used to wind up both himself and his team-mates by playing punk music including the Sex Pistols' 'Anarchy in the UK'?

5.   With which club did David Platt begin his league career?

6.   Of which club is pop superstar Robbie Williams a lifelong supporter?

7.   The most southerly home of an English club, this is the second largest city after Hull not to have played in the top flight – which club plays there?

8.   Which was the first major football competition in England to be sponsored?

9.   The world's oldest ground is the Drill Field – which Conference side plays there?

10. Which is the only British club to win the European Champions Cup more times than it's won its own League Championship?

11. Who missed a penalty against Wimbledon in December 1998 on the same day as he won the BBC Sports Personality of the Year Award?

12. Who scored against Chelsea for FC Copenhagen in October 1998 and later joined the Stamford Bridge club?

13. Which club signed the Chinese internationals Fan Zhiyi and Sun Jhai?

14. Steve Staunton has had two spells at two clubs, Liverpool is one, who are the other?

15. Which Nationwide Division One player did Rangers buy in 2001?

BRITISH CLUBS

1.　Which club's ground is the Madejski stadium named after its millionaire Chairman John Madejski?

2.　For which Caribbean country does Manchester City's Shaun Goater play international football?

3.　Which current England international scored a club record 93 league goals for Millwall?

4.　Of which club is TV presenter Nick Hancock a devoted follower?

5.　Who when moving to Arsenal in January 1995 for £2.5million became Britain's most expensive teenager?

6.　Who captained Scotland at the 1998 World Cup Finals?

7.　Which player was the subject of the nickname in the headline 'Ball gets Kinky?

8.　Which Partick Thistle goalkeeper played 410 league games for the club and won 51 Scottish caps?

9.　Which London club came closest to winning the Championship when finishing runners-up in 1975–76?

10.　Which Welsh side reached the FA Cup Semi-Final in 1964 only to lose to Preston?

11.　Which club won the Scottish League in 1958 with a record 132 goals and conceded just 29 goals?

12.　Which club dropped from the top flight into Division Four between 1972–5 to become the first former League Champions to be relegated to the bottom Division?

13.　What was unusual about Jan Molby's hat-trick against Coventry in 1986?

14.　For which club did Ian Rush score his final goal in the FA Cup, in a third round tie at Goodison Park in 1998?

15.　Which Division Three side in the 2000–1 season last appeared in the English top flight in the 1970–71 season?

CHELSEA

1. Who replaced Ruud Gullit in February 1998 and helped them to a European Cup Winners Cup success?

2. Who kept goal for the club in all but one league game in 1999–2000?

3. Which Chelsea player was the first player to score four goals in a Premiership game in 2000–2001?

4. Of the 26 players in the 1997 FA Cup final only one was an England international, who was the Chelsea player?

5. Which club knocked Chelsea, the holders, out of the FA Cup in 1998 in the third round, winning 5–3 at Stamford Bridge?

6. Which man made four FA Cup final appearances in his career as a player – three with Tottenham and one with Chelsea?

7. Which defender played for Barcelona against Man Utd in the 1991 Cup Winners Cup final and played for Chelsea in 2000–2001?

8. Who in July 1998 moved from Rangers to Chelsea on a free transfer?

9. Which future Chelsea player won a treble of awards in 1995 – FIFA World Player, African Player and European Player Of The Year?

10. Who scored both their goals in the FA Cup semi-final defeat of Luton in 1994?

11. Which legendary player scored a club record 41 league goals in 1960–1?

12. Which player scored 12 league penalties when Chelsea won the Second Division in 1988–9?

13. Which Second Division side did Chelsea beat 5–1 in their 1970 FA Cup semi-final, the last time five goals were scored by one team as that stage of the competition?

14. Which former Arsenal player managed Chelsea to their only League Championship success in 1955?

15. Who scored after just 27 seconds as Chelsea beat Man Utd 5–0 in October 1999, his only league goal for the club?

FULHAM

1. Which club knocked Fulham out of the FA Cup in 2001?

2. Who is the current manager of the club?

3. Who was the only Fulham player in the England World Cup winning side in 1966?

4. During 1997–8 who did Fulham appoint as chief operating officer?

5. Fulham won their first 11 league games in 2000–2001 before being held to a draw at Molineux –who was this against?

6. Which former Scottish international joined the club for £2million in the summer of 2000?

7. In 1997–8 Fulham paid a record fee of £1million for which player from West Brom?

8. Who scored twice in a European Cup final and joined Fulham in September 1999?

9. In 1998–99 Fulham were knocked out of the FA Cup 1–0 in Round 5 by Man Utd – who scored that goal?

10. Which current Premiership manager made his league debut as a player in 1951 with Fulham?

11. Who played for Newcastle in their 1999 FA Cup run and joined the Craven Cottage club from Metz in 2000?

12. Who left Craven Cottage in the summer of 2000 and played in the final of the Worthington Cup in February 2001?

13. This player played in a record 594 games for the club and is their most internationally-honoured player with 56 England caps?

14. Which current TV pundit scored on his league debut for Fulham against Aston Villa in March 1963 before going on to win England caps?

15. In the post-war era Fulham have been managed by both a father and his son – who are they?

THE CUPS – General

1.   Who scored a rare headed goal that gave West Ham United victory in the FA Cup Final in 1980?

2.   Which Chelsea player in 1997 won a record fourth FA Cup winner's medal at Wembley?

3.   Which side were beaten 4–0 by Manchester United in the 1996 Charity Shield only to gain revenge by winning a League match 5–0 a couple of months later?

4.   Which American played in goal for Leicester City in their 1997 League Final triumph over Middlesbrough?

5.   Who were the only side to concede four goals in an FA Cup Final in the 1980s – doing so in a replay?

6.   The Screen Sport Super Cup was played in 1985–86 for those English clubs who would have qualified for Europe. Which side beat Everton 7–2 on aggregate in the final?

7.   Who made a memorable double save in the 1973 FA Cup final for Sunderland against Leeds?

8.   Which defender scored a rare goal in scoring the winner for Liverpool in their 1981 League Cup final replay against West Ham?

9.   Which club won or shared the FA Charity Shield in 4 consecutive years from 1984–87?

10. Who scored the winning goal for Leeds United in three FA Cup semi-finals in 1965, 1970 and 1973?

11. Who was the Liberian-born player who played for Arsenal in the 1998 FA Cup Final against Newcastle?

12. Who captained Aston Villa to victory in the 1996 League Cup final and was in the 1998 Middlesbrough side beaten by Chelsea in the final of the same competition?

13. Which club won the FA Cup three times in the 1950s and have not won the competition since?

14. Which current First Division club was the only team to appear in a League Cup final in the 1960s, 1970s and 1980s?

15. Which goalkeeper appeared in four Charity Shields for Manchester City from 1968 to 1973 but failed to win either a League Championship or FA Cup winner's medal for the club?

FA CUP – THE 90s

1. In 1998 which Arsenal player became the second Dutchman to score in the final?

2. Which goalkeeper during the decade matched the feat of Dick Pym (of Bolton) by winning three FA Cup winner's medals without conceding a goal?

3. Which defender was the only player to appear in Manchester United's cup winning sides of 1990, 1994 and 1996?

4. Who was the Nigerian international who scored twice after coming on as a substitute for Everton in their 4–1 defeat of Spurs in their 1995 semi-final at Elland Road?

5. Which Fourth Division side famously knocked out the mighty Arsenal in the third round in 1992?

6. Which player scored for Manchester United in both the 1990 and 1994 finals?

7. In the 1991 final who was the Nottingham Forest player fouled by Paul Gascoigne in the incident that saw him carried off?

8. Who during the decade became only the second manager to lose FA Cup finals with different clubs (his first loss being in the 1980s)?

9. Who lifted the FA Cup as captain during the decade despite being substituted, due to injury, just nine minutes into the game?

10. Who appeared for the losing finalists Crystal Palace in 1990 and Sheffield Wednesday in 1993?

11. Who scored a memorable hat-trick as a substitute for Spurs in a 6–2 win at Southampton in 1994–95, after they were two goals down?

12. In the 1990–91 FA Cup who became the first full back in history to score in both the semi-final and final?

13. Which side, which included Dion Dublin in their line-up, was the last old Fourth Division side to reach the quarter-finals, doing so in 1989–90?

14. Which Newcastle player in 1998 made Cup history by becoming the first player to lose in finals with three different clubs?

15. Who in 1994 became only the second player-manager to appear in an FA Cup final?

THE UEFA CUP

1. Which English side won the UEFA Cup twice during the 1970s, against Borussia Moenchengladbach and Bruges?

2. Which was the last British side to appear in the two-legged version of the final, doing so in 1987?

3. In 1979–80 which country uniquely provided all four semi-finalists in the competition?

4. Which side did Arsenal lose to in the 2000 UEFA Cup Final?

5. Whose final game in charge of Spurs was when they lifted the trophy in 1984?

6. Which English side won the competition in 1969 after finishing tenth in Division One the previous year?

7. Which England international appeared in the 1997 UEFA Cup Final for Inter Milan against Schalke 04?

8. When Bayern Munich lifted the trophy in 1996, which former Premiership star scored a European record 15 goals for them in the competition?

9. After the ban was lifted on playing in Europe in 1990–91, which English side appeared in the UEFA Cup but lost 3–2 on aggregate to Inter Milan in the second round?

10. Which side, later to defeat Juventus in a European Cup final, lost to the Italian side in the UEFA Cup Final in 1993?

11. Which side did Spurs play in the only all-English European final in history in 1972?

12. Who scored 14 goals for Ipswich when they won the competition in 1980–81?

13. Which Spanish club won the competition in both 1962 and 1963?

14. In the 1970–71 semi-final who became the only English side to defeat Liverpool at Anfield in a European match?

15. Who scored for Inter Milan when they beat Lazio 3–0 in the 1998 final having scored the only goal for Barcelona in the 1997 Cup Winners Cup final?

EUROPEAN CLUBS – General

1.   Hadjuk Split has won which country's league title on nine occasions?

2.   Which Dutchman's transfer to Manchester United in 2000 was called off due to fitness problems?

3.   Against which club did Leeds record a 4–1 away win in the Champions Cup in 2000–1 to qualify for the knock-out stages?

4.   Which Italian star set a new world record transfer fee of £7.7 million when moving from Fiorentina to Juventus just prior to the 1990 World Cup finals?

5.   Which club have won the most major European trophies – 10 in total – prior to the start of the 2000–1 season?

6.   Which legendary player was manager of Barcelona when they won the European Cup in 1992?

7.   The best Turkish player of all time, he has played for Galatasaray and has been the leading scorer in the Turkish First Division three times – who is he?

8.   Which current Premiership manager was the manager of Fiorentina between 1993 and 1997?

9.   With which club did Sven Goran Eriksson have two spells in charge, the first being from 1982–84?

10.   With which club has Italian star Francesco Totti played for his entire career?

11.   Which player joined Newcastle United after playing in the 1998 World Cup final and being the leading goalscorer in France in 1996–97 and 1997–98?

12.   What nationality was Florian Albert, the 1967 European Footballer of the Year?

13.   Now currently Italian team manager, he won 20 major trophies as a club boss including all three major European trophies?

14.   Which club have won the Bundesliga on four occasions, the last time in 1997–98, but have never appeared in a European final?

15.   For which German club did England striker Tony Woodcock play between 1979 and 1982?

ENGLAND

1. Which West Ham player followed his father into the England team when making his international debut against Belgium in 1999?

2. Which country in 1997 became the first to defeat England in a World Cup match at Wembley?

3. Which midfielder made 14 appearances for England from 1989 to 1992 whilst with Arsenal?

4. Which club did Don Revie leave to manage England in 1974?

5. Who scored his only hat-trick for England in a 8–0 win over Turkey in November 1984?

6. Who scored both England's goals in the 2–0 play-off win against Scotland at Hampden Park in November 1999?

7. 'Yanks 2 Planks 0' was a newspaper headline when England lost 2–0 to the USA during the 1990s – but what year did the game take place?

8. Two managers with the same surname have taken charge of England in full internationals, but what is it?

9. Which Division Two side (in 2000–1) provided both England's forwards in the 1984 international against France in Paris?

10. Which then Blackburn Rovers player made his England debut against the Cameroon at Wembley in November 1997?

11. Against which country did Alan Shearer score on his England debut in 1992 at Wembley?

12. In their opening game of the 1966 World Cup finals which country stopped England from scoring at Wembley for the first time?

13. Who made his 77th and final appearance for England when captaining them in the semi-final of Italia 90 versus Germany?

14. How many goals did Gary Lineker score for England in full internationals?

15. Who scored both of Chile's goals when they defeated England at Wembley in 1998?

BEST OF BRITISH

1. Who scored a record 28 goals in 73 internationals for Wales?

2. Who was the Northern Ireland manager in the 1982 and 1986 World Cup finals?

3. Who missed a penalty for Scotland in their Euro 96 game against England?

4. Which current player has won over 70 caps for Wales with ten different clubs?

5. Who won 88 caps for Northern Ireland from 1972–86 whilst with Man United, Stoke City and Man City?

6. Which current Everton player and his father have both played international football for Scotland?

7. Against Bulgaria in December 1994 who became the 50th player called Jones to be capped for Wales?

8. Who scored his only hat-trick for Northern Ireland against Cyprus in April 1971?

9. Which Leicester City player was sent-off for Scotland against the Faroe Islands in June 1999?

10. Later to manage Wales for just one game, he scored their last international hat-trick against Scotland in 1979. Who is he?

11. Who moved from Manchester United to Preston in the 2000–1 season after scoring twice on his Northern Ireland debut against Luxembourg Feb 2000?

12. Which Caribbean country defeated Scotland 1–0 in the 1990 World Cup Finals in Italy?

13. He was born in Belgium and won 13 caps for Wales whilst with Everton from 1985 to 1989?

14. Which player scored his only goal in the World Cup final stages for Northern Ireland against Algeria in 1986?

15. Which player scored for Scotland in the World Cup final stages of 1974, 1978 and 1982?

QUICKFIRE

1. Who left Bournemouth in 1991 for £350,000 and was Liverpool's captain in 2000–2001 despite being injured?

2. Former world 1500 metres champion Steve Cram supports which North East club?

3. Which player, who appeared for England in 2001, moved from Derby to Charlton in 1998?

4. Which England World Cup star of 1986 had at one stage played for Vancouver Whitecaps?

5. Who in 1986–7 managed both Manchester City and Aston Villa, in the season in which both sides were relegated?

6. Who were the brothers who were opposing goalkeepers when Preston played Bury in 1990?

7. Trevor Steven won Championship medals with Everton and Glasgow Rangers. Which French club did he also win a Championship medal with?

8. Formed in 1862, the oldest surviving club in the world was a founder member of the Football League – who are they?

9. In 1993 Keith Alexander became the first black manager in the history of the Football League - which club appointed him?

10. In 1997 which TV pundit turned down an opportunity to manage Everton?

11. In the 1998 World Cup which country's players dyed their hair blonde in a show of solidarity?

12. For which country does Stephane Henchoz play international football?

13. Which club went 29 games unbeaten from the start of the 1973–74 season in the top flight?

14. In the 1974 European Cup semi-final which club had three players sent-off and four booked in a game against Celtic?

15. Which 2000–1 Premiership side has suffered the worst defeat in Europe of any English side: 6–1 by Bayern Munich in 1970?

QUICKFIRE

1. The first all-seater stadium in England was Coventry's in 1981 – what is it called?

2. Eric Cantona won Championship medals with Leeds and Manchester United. Which French side was he with when they won their Championship?

3. Which was the last Scottish club to win a European trophy?

4. Which country finished bottom of England's group in the group stages in Euro 2000?

5. Who in 1987–8 managed both Watford and Sheffield United in a season in which both clubs were relegated?

6. Who at Anfield in October 1999 was sent-off for the ninth time in his Stamford Bridge career?

7. Who opened the scoring for Arsenal in their famous 2–0 win at Anfield that clinched the title in 1989?

8. Who scored a first-half hat-trick in the Manchester United-Arsenal clash at Old Trafford in February 2001?

9. For which player did QPR receive a club record £6 million fee in June 1995?

10. Which former Liverpool player was sent-off on his Coventry City debut in the 2000–1 season?

11. Which Celtic manager was voted Manager of the Year in 1966 and 1967?

12. Who were the cousins who played for Spurs in the 1987 FA Cup final?

13. Which North West club had two players sent-off in the 1994 Second Division play-off final at Wembley against Burnley?

14. Later a Liverpool player and TV personality he holds the Britsh record for scoring the quickest ever hat-trick, doing so for Motherwell in 1959 in two and a half minutes. Who is he?

15. The last hat-trick in an FA Cup semi-final was scored by which Manchester United player in 1958?

The Group phase

1. Peter Shilton is England's most capped player with 125 caps – but with which five clubs did he win them? (5 points)

2. Which four clubs won the League Cup on two occasions during the 1970s? (4 points)

3. In the 1999–2000 season, for the first time in over 20 years, three teams had average league gates of more than 40,000 in England – who were they? (3 points)

Penalty Shoot-out

1. Who was the former Preston and England international knighted in 1997?

2. Who played in and managed victorious Brazilian World Cup winning sides?

3. Which man has twice been the most expensive player bought by an English club, in 1992 and 1996?

4. Who was the manager of Crystal Palace between 1976 and 1980?

5. Which club reached the FA Cup final in 1966 without conceding a goal – the first to do so in the 20th century?

Full-time

The greatest number of goals scored in a career has been the source of great debate in recent years. Although Artur Friedenreich and the great Pele both claimed over 1000 goals in Brazilian football, many of these were in unofficial friendlies. Ferenc Puskas is regarded as the highest goal-scorer in what are termed official games, with 551 from 1943–66. The highest by a player based predominately in England is the 474 scored by John Aldridge.

Gerry Francis gets his boats mixed up over QPR's injury crisis: 'There's more ice in the dressing room than sank the Bismarck'

Chelsea 1970 FA Cup hero David Webb was not allowed to receive his winner's medal after the game. He had swapped shirts with a Leeds player, and as a result an official would not allow him up to the director's box to collect his medal, believing him to be a from the Leeds team. He eventually obtained his reward in the dressing room.

The Group phase

1. Since 1980 five England international goalkeepers have won FA Cup winners' medals – who are they?
    (5 points)

2. Which five clubs have won the European Cup at Wembley?
    (5 points)

3. At the start of the 2000–1 season two pairs of Premiership managers had the same surnames – which two surnames are they?
    (2 points)

Penalty Shoot-out

1. Which club set a record for the 20th century in 1990–91 by losing just one league game all season?

2. Which Ipswich Town player captained England in the 1982 World Cup finals?

3. Who was the manager of Wimbledon when they were promoted to the top flight in 1986?

4. Which midfielder won the first of 51 caps for Wales in 1976 whilst with Wrexham and was capped with six other sides in a colourful career??

5. Which Manchester City player in 1955 and 1956 was the first player to score in successive FA Cup finals at Wembley?

Full-time

The ball famously burst in the 1946 FA Cup final between Derby County and Charlton Athletic. However it is less well known that, in the league match between the clubs in the following week, the ball burst again.

Terry McDermott on Newcastle being drawn against Arsenal: 'Nobody hands you cups on a plate.'

The youngest player to appear for Wales is called Ryan and his surname does begin with the letter 'G', but it is Ryan Green of Wolves who holds the record when appearing against Malta in June 1998 aged 17 years 226 days. He was 106 days younger than the previous holder, the other Ryan 'G' of Manchester United and Wales, who debuted in 1991.

BRITISH CLUBS

1. Who was the former Man Utd winger who scored for Man City against Liverpool in the 2000–1 FA Cup?

2. Which club won the FA Cup in 1901, 1921, 1961, 1981 and 1991?

3. Who is the Australian goalkeeper who has played for Aston Villa and Manchester United?

4. Which club received a record transfer fee of £1million from Man Utd in August 1992 for Dion Dublin?

5. Two Argentineans joined Tottenham in 1978 - Ossie Ardiles and who else?

6. Which England star of the 1986 World Cup began his career with Carlisle United and won trophies with Liverpool?

7. Which player won 43 caps for Romania whilst playing for Chelsea?

8. Which famous manager led Oxford United from the Southern League to the old Second Division before hanging up his playing boots in 1971?

9. Who in July 1996 became the most expensive teenager in British football when he joined Leeds for £2.6million from Charlton?

10. Which was the first English club to lay down a so-called 'plastic pitch' for the start of the 1981–2 season?

11. Which club in 1983–4 set a League record playing 31 consecutive matches without winning a game?

12. Tony Kay, Peter Swan and Bronco Layne were all banned from football in the 1960s after a betting scandal at which club?

13. Which team has appeared in the most Charity Shields?

14. Which Dutchman was sent-off against Belgium in their 1998 World Cup match?

15. In the 1998–99 FA Cup match between Arsenal and Sheffield United, which Arsenal player's 'goal' led to the game being replayed?

BRITISH CLUBS

1. Who in February 2001 stepped down as manager of QPR for the second time in seven years?

2. Which player was left out of his club's European game against Lyon in 2001 because of his fear of flying?

3. Who in 1996 became the first Colombian to play in the Football League when he joined Newcastle?

4. Who in 1988 took over from Kenny Sansom at the age of just 21 to become Arsenal captain?

5. Who are the Cumbrians who play at Brunton Park?

6. Who was the first 50 year old to play in the top flight of English football?

7. Name the only FA Cup-winning captain of the 1990s who never won an international cap?

8. Which international manager was in charge of Leeds United for 44 days in October 1978?

9. Who is the Tranmere player whose throw-in reached 46.3 metres (50.5 yards) in 1997–8?

10. Which future England player with QPR and Spurs is still Cambridge United's youngest-ever player, a record set in 1982 when he was aged just 16 years 228 days?

11. By 1994 which was the last English club still playing on a plastic pitch?

12. In February 1970 which player returned from suspension and scored six times against Northampton in the FA Cup?

13. Which England defender made his first international appearance for six years against France in February 1999, when aged 35?

14. Which England international joined David Platt on loan when he was coach at Sampdoria?

15. Which current Division One side last appeared in the top flight in 1987–88?

WEST HAM UNITED

1. All four England goals in the 1966 World Cup final were scored by West Ham players. Geoff Hurst scored three, of course, but who got the other?

2. Which West Ham striker in 2000–2001 equalled a post-war record of scoring in ten consecutive matches whilst on loan with Bournemouth?

3. Which club defeated West Ham 7–1 in a league game on April Fools Day 2000?

4. Who was transferred for a record fee when he moved from Upton Park and joined Everton for £2.2million in 1988?

5. Which club in 1997–8 knocked West Ham out of both the League Cup and FA Cup (in the sixth round on penalties)?

6. Who made his West Ham debut against Manchester United in January 1999 aged 17?

7. Which former West Ham player appeared in Birmingham's Worthington Cup final side in February 2001?

8. In 1998–9 two West Ham players played for England against the Czech Republic. Rio Ferdinand was one. Who was the other?

9. Who won 47 England caps between 1974–82, scoring five goals, whilst with West Ham?

10. Who has managed both West Ham and England?

11. Who in 1968 against Sunderland became the last player to score six goals in a top-flight league game in England?

12. Against which club did the Hammers become the first side to taste defeat in an FA Cup final in 1923?

13. Who scored both the goals when West Ham won the Cup Winners Cup in 1965?

14. Who in the 1972–3 season scored two goals in a match eight times, all on Saturdays?

15. Which Scotsman, famed for his fearsome penalties, played in West Ham's 1980 FA Cup-winning side?

CHARLTON ATHLETIC

1.   Who took over as manager of the club in June 1995?

2.   Which South African scored twice for the club in the 3–3 draw with Man Utd in December 2000?

3.   From which club did Charlton sign Jonatan Johansson in the close season in 2000?

4.   Who top scored for the club when they won the First Division in 1999–2000 with 24 league goals?

5.   Name either of the two grounds that Charlton played their home games at before returning to the Valley in 1992?

6.   What is the club's nickname, which comes from a chip shop that used to be frequented by the players in the early 1900's?

7.   Which current Newcastle and England player scored on his Charlton debut in 1984 and helped the club to promotion in 1986?

8.   Who was the last Charlton player to win (in 1965) an England cap prior to 2001, and later became manager in 1979?

9.   Who scored a hat trick in Charlton's first-ever Premiership game at home in August 1998 against Southampton?

10.   Which club defeated Charlton by a single goal in the Full Members Cup final in 1986–87?

11.   John Hewie won 19 caps for Scotland but in which country was he born?

12.   Who played for both Tottenham and Fulham in FA Cup finals and managed Charlton between 1981–1982?

13.   Charlton were once 5–1 down in a match in 1957 yet still ended up winning 7–6, against which club managed by Bill Shankly?

14.   One of the great goalkeepers, he made a record 583 appearances for the club from 1934–1956 – who is he?

15.   Name either of the clubs Charlton played in successive FA Cup finals in 1946 and 1947?

THE LEAGUE CUP

1. Later to move to Liverpool, he scored Leicester City's equaliser in the drawn final against Middlesbrough in 1997?

2. Liverpool won the competition for four years from 1981–84 and also in 1995. Which man set a competition record by playing in all five finals for the Reds?

3. For which club did Nigel Jemson score the only goal of the game in a League Cup final?

4. Who scored twice for Aston Villa when they defeated Manchester United 3–1 in the final in 1994?

5. Who made three consecutive appearances in the final for Oldham and Manchester United from 1990–92?

6. Which England forward scored for West Brom in the finals of 1966 and 1970?

7. Who was the only player to appear in Tottenham's winning side in the 1999 final to have played for Spurs in the 1991 FA Cup final?

8. A star of the 2000 European Championships he opened the scoring for Aston Villa in their 3–0 win over Leeds in the 1996 final?

9. Which London club has reached the semi-finals on two occasions – losing to Leicester City in 1997 and Tottenham in 1999?

10. Now at Celtic, he scored Bolton's goal in their defeat by Liverpool in the 1995 final?

11. What was the surname of the brothers who appeared for Luton when they won the trophy against Arsenal in 1988?

12. At which ground was the Nottingham Forest-Liverpool final settled in 1978 after a 0–0 draw at Wembley?

13. Which future Manchester United player appeared for Nottingham Forest in the 1992 final against United?

14. Which Scottish international appeared for the final for West Brom (1970), Man City (1976) and Norwich City (1985)?

15. During the 1980s who was the first player-manager to appear in the final?

FA CUP – General

1. Who with Liverpool and Spurs is the only goalkeeper to appear in five FA Cup finals at Wembley?

2. Which Manchester United player in 1994 became the only player to score twice from the spot in an FA Cup Final?

3. Apart from Juninho, which other Brazilian player appeared for Middlesbrough in the 1997 FA Cup Final?

4. Nicknamed 'Killer', he captained Coventry to victory in the 1987 FA Cup Final – who is he?

5. Which player scored for Newcastle United in their 1998 and 1999 FA Cup semi-final wins?

6. Who was the Nottingham Forest goalkeeper who saved Gary Lineker's penalty in the 1991 FA Cup final?

7. Which full-back was the only player to appear in all of Arsenal's five FA Cup finals from 1971–80, lifting the trophy as captain in 1979?

8. Which side won the FA Cup in both the 1960s and 1970s with a side composed entirely of players born in England?

9. Which side in the 1970s was the last FA Cup-winning side not to contain an international player?

10. Apart from Gary Lineker, which other player appeared for Everton in the 1986 final and Spurs in the 1991 final?

11. Who was the only manager of FA Cup-winning sides in both the 1960s and 1970s?

12. Which player scored for Leeds United in both the 1970 Cup final and replay?

13. Which player has made the most appearances in the FA Cup during a career, 88 from 1959–81, winning medals with Liverpool in 1965 and 1974?

14. What was unusual about the 16 goals scored in the three FA Cup semi-final matches of 1990 – Man United 3, Oldham 3 (and 2–1 in replay) and Crystal Palace 4 Liverpool 3?

15. Which non-league side reached the FA Cup fourth round in 1983–84 and fifth round in 1984–85?

BRITISH CLUBS IN EUROPE

1. Who was Leeds top scorer in the first group stage of the Champions Cup in 2000–1?

2. Which English club won the European Super Cup in 1982–83 by defeating Barcelona 3–1 on aggregate?

3. Which English side was knocked out of the UEFA Cup in 2000–1 by the lowly Swiss side St Gallen?

4. Which English club played in Europe for the first time in 1994–95 in the UEFA Cup but lost 3–2 on aggregate to Trelleborg of Sweden?

5. Which Dutchman scored for Ipswich in both legs of the 1981 UEFA Cup final?

6. Which English club played in the European Cup for the only time in 1968–69 losing to Turkish side Fenerbahce in the first round?

7. Which British club knocked defending champions Ipswich out of the UEFA Cup in 1981–82?

8. Which player appeared for Chelsea in the 1971 Cup Winners Cup final and played for Arsenal in the final again nine years later?

9. Who in 1996 against Vladikavkaz became the second Rangers player to score a hat-trick in a European Champions Cup game?

10. Why were QPR forced to play their UEFA Cup matches in 1984–85 at Highbury?

11. Which English club has played in the UEFA Cup in a record 11 seasons?

12. Which French side did Arsenal beat in the semi-finals of the UEFA Cup in 1999–2000?

13. Which Anderlecht player scored twice against West Ham in the 1976 Cup Winners Cup final and later moved to the Hammers?

14. Which Republic of Ireland international scored for Everton in their Cup Winners Cup final triumph over Rapid Vienna in 1985?

15. Which was the only English side to win a European trophy in the 1960s, 1970s and 1980s?

EUROPEAN CHAMPIONS CUP

1. Who was the Liverpool manager on the first three occasions they won the trophy?

2. In which city did Manchester United complete the historic treble in 1999?

3. Which current Arsenal player appeared for Ajax when they won the trophy in 1995?

4. Who was the manager of Aston Villa when they won the competition in 1982?

5. Who scored the only goal of the game when Nottingham Forest won the trophy for the first time in 1979?

6. Later to manage Barcelona, he led Ajax to victory in the competition in 1995?

7. Which side has appeared in seven finals but won the trophy on just two occasions, both in the 1960s?

8. Which Bayern Munich forward was the leading goalscorer in the European Cup for three consecutive seasons from 1972 to 1975?

9. Which is the only team to have played over 200 matches in the competition?

10. In which city did Liverpool win the trophy on two occasions?

11. Which great Italian sweeper captained AC Milan to victory in the final in both 1989 and 1990?

12. Which side did Leeds defeat 6–0 at Elland Road in the first round group stage in the 2000–1 Champions League?

13. Which side has appeared against three different English clubs in the final of the competition?

14. Which English side first appeared in the competition in 1972–73, but lost to Juventus in the semi-finals ?

15. Who was the England international who appeared against Liverpool in the 1981 final for Real Madrid?

WORLD CUP –1990s

1. Which player scored twice for France in the 1998 World Cup Final against Brazil?

2. Who scored twice for Italy in their 1994 semi-final against Bulgaria?

3. Which country shocked the holders Argentina 1–0 in the opening game of the 1990 tournament?

4. Which country defeated Germany 3–0 in their 1998 quarter-final clash?

5. Which city staged the famous England-West Germany semi-final in 1990?

6. Who played for the Cameroon in the finals of 1982, 1990 and 1994?

7. Scotland recorded a single victory in the 1990 finals – beating which side 2–1 in a group game?

8. Who was the charismatic goalkeeper who starred for Paraguay in the 1998 Finals?

9. In the 1990 match against Egypt who became the first defender to score for England in the finals since 1962?

10. West Germany won the 1990 World Cup but who was their leading scorer in the finals with four goals?

11. Whose appearance as a substitute for the Republic of Ireland against Mexico in 1994 led to much 'industrial language' from Jack Charlton to officials?

12. In 1998 who created World Cup history by scoring for two different countries in the finals when scoring for Croatia, having scored for Yugoslavia in 1990?

13. In 1990 which goalkeeper set a new World Cup record by keeping his tenth clean sheet in the finals, having kept his first in 1982?

14. In 1994 which country did Brazil play twice in the competition – in the group stages and in the semi-final?

15. Which European country went out on penalties in the World Cups of 1990,1994 and 1998?

WORLD CUP – 1980s

1. Who scored a famous hat-trick when Italy defeated Brazil 3–2 in the 1982 World Cup Finals?

2. Who was the German goalkeeper involved in the infamous incident with Frenchman Patrick Battiston in the 1982 World Cup semi-final?

3. After West Germany in 1970 which was the next country to defeat England in a World Cup finals match?

4. Who played for Northern Ireland aged just 17 years 41 days in 1982, making him the youngest to appear in the tournament?

5. Who played his 119th and final match for Northern Ireland against Brazil 1986?

6. Which Argentinean was sent off in the Argentina-Brazil match in 1982?

7. Which African side shocked West Germany 2–1 in the group stages in 1982?

8. Which Spanish forward equalled the World Cup record by scoring four times in the match against Denmark in 1986?

9. Which country recorded their best performance in the World Cup by reaching the semi-final stage in 1986, but lost 2–0 to Argentina?

10. Which country set a World Cup record by defeating El Salvador 10–1 in the 1982 finals?

11. England went out of the World Cup in 1982 after failing to beat which country in their final game?

12. In the 1982 Northern Ireland-Spain clash who became the first British player sent-off in the finals?

13. In 1982 and 1986, who captained the losers Germany in the World Cup Final, the only man to captain a losing team twice in the Final?

14. Which was the only country to score against England in their five matches in the 1982 World Cup finals?

15. Who was the 1986 European Footballer of the Year who scored a hat-trick for Russia against Belgium in that year's final stages but was still on the losing side?

QUICKFIRE

1.   What nationality is Leeds United's Harry Kewell?

2.   Which current Scottish Premier League manager captained Northern Ireland in the 1982 World Cup finals?

3.   To which Italian club did Paul Gascoigne move in 1992?

4.   Where did John Barnes score one of England's greatest goals in 1984?

5.   Who resigned his position in 1994 as manager of one London club to take over at Tottenham?

6.   Britain's most northerly league football ground is Pittodrie – which club plays there?

7.   Who was the first Welshman to win 90 international caps?

8.   Who is the former player who is now the Chief Executive of the PFA - the players union?

9.   Who was the first Nigerian international player to win a FA Cup winner's medal?

10. Who made over 600 appearances for his one club AC Milan in defence, won 81 caps for Italy, and captained them in the 1990 World Cup?

11. Who won League Championship medals with Arsenal and Everton and won his only England cap whilst with Aston Villa?

12. Which England international retired after losing an eye in a car accident in 1972?

13. Which Manchester United player was sent-off twice in five days in September 1998 against Barcelona and Arsenal?

14. What happened when Derby County played their first game at Pride Park against Wimbledon in August 1997?

15. Who was the first foreign manager of a Scottish League Championship-winning side?

QUICKFIRE

1. Who has been the Chelsea chairman throughout the 1990s?

2. Barnet's most famous son is the cheeky cockney who managed the club in the 1980s and 1990. Who is he?

3. Who made his Republic of Ireland debut in 1986 aged 28 and was the manager of a First Division side in 2000–1?

4. Which club has won the Portuguese League on the most occasions?

5. Who scored Real Zaragoza's winning goal against Arsenal in the Cup Winners Cup final in 1995?

6. Which was the last club to reach the FA Cup final at Wembley for the first time?

7. Who was the player David Beckham petulantly kicked out at during France 98 and was then sent off?

8. Who made his England debut in 1995 versus Japan after just 19 games for his club – the fewest by an England debutant, at that time, since the war?

9. In the qualifying draw for Euro 2000, with which country were England paired for the fifth consecutive qualifying tournament?

10. Which Rangers player scored 20 goals in nine matches during the 1997–98 season?

11. Which Portuguese club has been managed by Graeme Souness?

12. Former British tennis star David Lloyd once took over control of which English club?

13. Which great England centre-forward was known as the 'Lion of Vienna'?

14. Which Hibernian player is an international team-mate of Dwight Yorke?

15. Bulgarian World Cup goalkeeper Boris Mikhailov played for which English club side?

The Group phase

1.   Which three current players have scored 150 or more goals
      in Serie A matches?
      (3 points)

2.   Who are the four players born in Scotland to have scored
      in a European Champions Cup final?
      (4 points)

3.   For which five clubs has Andy Cole played in his career?
      (5 points)

Penalty Shoot-out

1.   Which was the only English side to be managed by Sir
      Stanley Matthews?

2.   Which player scored a record six hat-tricks for England in
      post-war internationals?

3.   Emlyn Hughes managed which club when they were
      relegated to the Third Division in 1983?

4.   Which opponents of England in the 1966 World Cup did
      Sir Alf Ramsey brand 'animals' for their brutal approach
      in the quarter-final?

5.   What Australian city gives its name to Leyton Orient's
      ground?

Full-time

The only known instance of a father and son playing in the same international match came in 1996 when Arnor Gudjohnsen (aged 35) was replaced by current Chelsea star Eidur (17) for Iceland during a game against Estonia. Mr Gudjohnsen senior is best remembered as the Anderlecht player whose missed penalty in the 1984 UEFA Cup final gave the trophy to Spurs.

Barnsley's Macedonian striker Georgi Hristov on the attractiveness of the local population: 'The local girls are far uglier than the girls in Belgrade. Besides they don't drink as much beer as the Barnsley girls.'

Visitors to Ipswich Town had better be careful they have not fallen foul of the taxman, for the car park at Portman Road is owned by the Inland Revenue.

The Group phase

1. Which three clubs since the start of the Premiership in 1992, and up to the end of the 2000–1 season, had played in the Premiership, Division One and Division Two?
    (3 points)

2. From 1990–2000 inclusive four players scored in two different FA Cup finals (excluding replays). Who were they?
    (4 points)

3. Apart from Aberdeen, which five Scottish clubs begin with the letter 'A'?
    (5 points)

Penalty Shoot-out

1. From which club did Spurs sign Teddy Sheringham in 1992?

2. Which non-league club do you associate with both Stuart Pearce and Vinnie Jones?

3. Which Arsenal defender was sent-off in a FA Cup semi-final against Spurs in 1993?

4. Who was the legendary player who won 31 caps between 1947 and 1961 for Argentina (8) and Spain (23)?

5. For which club did John Gregory play in a FA Cup final during the 1980s?

Full-time

After beating Bradford City on 20 November 1999, Leeds United went ten consecutive Saturdays without playing a fixture, due to midweek European fixtures and TV games.

Conversation between Liverpool fans and England singing star John Barnes:

Fans - 'Hey Barnesy, give us one of your raps'

JB - 'I'm afraid my singing days are over'

Fans – 'The way you played today your football days are over as well.'

The penalty missed by Sinisa Mihajlovic for Yugoslavia against Holland in 1998 was the first miss, during open play, in the finals since Enzo Scifo for Belgium against Spain in 1990.

BRITISH CLUBS

1.   Which club does TV presenter Angus Deayton support?

2.   Who scored for Chelsea in both league games against Man
      Utd in 2000–2001 and also the Charity Shield?

3.   Which future international manager took Watford from
      Division Four to runners up in Division One between 1977
      and 1983?

4.   In 1983–84 which Liverpool player became the first for
      six years to score 30 league goals in the First Division?

5.   From which club did Chris Waddle move to Spurs in
      1985?

6.   Which Division One side play at Bramall Lane?

7.   Which future England goalkeeper made his league debut
      with Southampton in 1986 in a match they lost 5–1 to
      Manchester United?

8.   Who played 14 games for Torquay before moving to Man
      Utd in 1988 for £180,000 and going on to win England
      caps?

9.   Neil Finn in January 1996 became the Premiership's
      youngest player at 17 years three days – which club did he
      play for?

10.   Which lower league side beat Man Utd 3–0 at Old
      Trafford in the League Cup in 1995–6 – United's only
      home defeat all season?

11.   Which non league side defeated West Brom 4–2 at the
      Hawthorns in the FA Cup in 1991 before going out in the
      next round to Everton?

12.   Who in 1986–87 scored a hat trick for Belgium against
      Scotland and then came on as a substitute in the FA Cup
      final for Spurs?

13.   Who won a Championship winners medal with
      Nottingham Forest in 1978 and Aston Villa in 1981?

14.   Which former West Brom defender is deputy chairman of
      the Professional Footballers' Association?

15.   Which club in March 1989 missed three penalties and
      scored one whilst their opponents Brighton scored a
      penalty?

BRITISH CLUBS

1. Which Midlands club does TV presenter Frank Skinner support?

2. Which club were originally called Dial Square and in 1931 became the first London club to win the English League title?

3. How many goals did Eric Cantona score in three FA Cup finals for Man Utd?

4. Which Newcastle defender in 1992 used to somersault in the air in order to gain more distance on a throw-in?

5. Who won a Championship medal with Liverpool in 1973 and Nottingham Forest in 1978?

6. Which Liverpool player was the Division One leading goalscorer in 1987–88 with 26 goals?

7. Which player moved from Newcastle United to Liverpool for a record £1.7 million fee in 1987?

8. With which club did Nick Barmby make his Premiership debut in 1992?

9. Whose move to Coventry City in 1999 from Wolves for £6 million made him the most expensive teenager in British football?

10. Which club played its first ever game in the top flight in England in August 1986?

11. Who scored Everton's winner against Wimbledon with just nine minutes left of the 1993–4 season to guarantee their survival in the top flight?

12. Which Graham Taylor led side finished runner-up to Liverpool in the 1989–90 Championship race?

13. Which current Premiership side has played in four Wembley FA Cup Finals but have still to win the trophy?

14. Who was the first player to score four goals in a Premiership game on two occasions?

15. Which club joined the League in 1987, drawing their first match against Wolves?

NOTTINGHAM FOREST

1. Nicknamed 'Psycho' he is the club's most capped
    international – who is he?

2. Who missed Nottingham Forest's first 11 league games of
    the 1998–9 season after a quarrel with the club?

3. Which goalkeeper was named Forest's Player of the Year in
    the 1999–2000 season?

4. In 1978 who were Forest's opponents in the first ever all-
    English tie in the European Champions Cup?

5. Who was Brian Clough's managerial partner who later
    went on to manage Derby County?

6. Who managed the FA Cup winners on two occasions in
    the 1980s and retired as manager of Forest in 1999?

7. Who in 1978 became the only Forest player to be awarded
    the Writers' Player of the Year?

8. Which forward moved from Forest to Manchester United
    for a £1.25 million fee in 1980?

9. In April 1995 Forest set a Premiership record for the
    biggest away win – who did they beat 7–1?

10. Who was the first Italian to play in the Premiership when
    he joined Forest for the 1995–6 season?

11. The League Managers' Association created their own
    Manager of the Year award in 1993 – which Forest
    manager won it in 1995?

12. Which player made a record 614 league appearances for
    the club 1951–1970?

13. Which much-travelled forward scored four times for Forest
    in a League Cup match in 1988 against QPR?

14. Nottingham Forest went 25 games unbeaten in the league
    until November 1995 when they lost 7–0 to which side?

15. Who was the former Derby favourite who came on as a
    substitute in the European Cup final win in 1980?

DERBY COUNTY

1.   Derby now play their home games at Pride Park but where did County play prior to the move?

2.   Who has managed the club since June 1995?

3.   For which country does Rory Delap play his international football?

4.   Deon Burton played for which country in the 1998 World Cup?

5.   Which defender in August 1998 became the most expensive Scotsman in history when moving from Derby to Blackburn Rovers for £5.3 million?

6.   Which former player in the Championship days of the 1970s returned to the club as coach during the 2000–1 season?

7.   In 1996–7 which overseas striker scored a spectacular goal on his debut, which helped the Rams defeat Man Utd at Old Trafford?

8.   Who against Italy in 2000 became Derby's first England cap for nearly ten years?

9.   Since 1970 two men have managed both Derby and Nottingham Forest – one is Brian Clough, who is the other?

10. Name the Birkenhead-born England defender who both played for and managed Derby County?

11. In 1976 Derby recorded their biggest win, 12–0, in their UEFA Cup encounter with which Irish side?

12. Which English international star once played for the Rams at the age of 42 years 164 days in 1992?

13. Which current Premiership manager was Derby's equal leading scorer in the 1987–88 season with just six goals?

14. Later to play for Derby and England, he scored 44 league goals for Bradford Park Avenue in the 1965–6 season?

15. Which goalkeeper kept goal in all 12 of the club's European Cup games in the 1970s?

THE LEAGUE CUP

1. Which player scored twice for Leicester City in the 2000 final when they won the trophy for the second time in four years?

2. Who was the Middlesbrough manager when they made their first final appearance in 1997?

3. Which then First Division side reached the final for the first time in 1995 but lost to Liverpool?

4. Who kept goal for Arsenal in the 1987 final and Leeds United in the 1996 final?

5. Who scored twice for Nottingham Forest in the final against Luton in 1989?

6. On which ground did Liverpool win the trophy in 1984?

7. Which man scored a record-equalling 49 goals in the competition from 1981–98?

8. Which side lost in the final, after two replays, to Aston Villa in 1977?

9. Who managed three different teams in the final of the competition – Norwich City, Man City and Aston Villa – in three successive finals from 1973 to 1975?

10. Which current Premiership club set a new competition record in 1983 by beating Bury 10–0?

11. Which year of the 1960s saw the first League Cup final staged at Wembley?

12. Which Premiership manager in the 2000–1 season appeared in finals during the 1960s for Aston Villa, Chelsea and Arsenal?

13. Who missed a penalty for Arsenal in their 1988 final loss to Luton Town?

14. Which full-back scored for Liverpool at Wembley in 1981 and 1983?

15. Whose memorable overhead kick gave Manchester City the trophy against Newcastle in 1976?

FA CUP – THE 1970s

1. Which club appeared in four FA Cup finals during the decade?

2. Which was the first Second Division side to win the competition in the decade?

3. Which ground staged the 1970 replayed final after Chelsea-Leeds drew 2–2 at Wembley?

4. Which non-league side famously defeated Newcastle United in the third round in 1972?

5. Who managed Arsenal when they completed the League and FA Cup double in 1971?

6. Who created history by winning FA Cup winner's medals in consecutive seasons with different clubs – with Ipswich in 1978 and Arsenal in 1979?

7. Who was the manager of Southampton when they lifted the trophy in 1976?

8. Which former Cup-winning skipper appeared for Fulham in the 1975 final?

9. When Liverpool defeated Newcastle in the 1974 final who scored twice for the Reds?

10. Who created Anglo-Scottish Cup history by captaining Aberdeen to the Scottish Cup in 1970 and Manchester United to the FA Cup in 1977?

11. Which player appeared in his fifth FA Cup final during the decade, four for Leeds and one for Manchester United in 1963?

12. Who managed different teams in finals during the decade – Chelsea in 1970 and Manchester United in 1979?

13. In 1975 who scored two goals for West Ham in the quarter-final, semi-final and the final itself?

14. Who was the Sunderland captain in 1973, the smallest player in history to lift the Cup?

15. Who commentated on the final on television for the first time in his broadcasting career in 1977?

SOUTH AMERICAN CLUBS

1. For which Brazilian club did Pele play for most of his career?

2. Nacional and Penarol have both won the World Club Championship, in which South American country do they play?

3. What is the name of the South American equivalent of the European Champions Cup?

4. In which South American country were a club called Everton the League Champions in 1950, 1952 and 1976?

5. Which South American country provided both the finalists in the 2000 FIFA World Club tournament?

6. Which Brazilian club was beaten 1–0 by Manchester United in the 1999 World Club Championship in Tokyo?

7. Which Argentinean club appeared in three consecutive World Club Championship matches from 1972–74 and defeated Liverpool 1–0 in the 1984 game?

8. In which stadium did Pele score the 1000th goal of his career, against Vasco de Gama in 1969?

9. Who was the Brazilian international striker who scored twice for Vasco de Gama against Manchester United in the 2000 FIFA World Club Championship?

10. Olimpia Asuncion won the World Club Championship in 1979 by defeating Malmo in the final. In which South American country do they play?

11. From which Argentinean club did Spurs buy Osvaldo Ardiles in 1978?

12. Which South American country's championship has been won by America Cali, Millonarios and Atletico Nacional Medelin?

13. From which Argentinean club did Barcelona buy Diego Maradona in 1982, a club he later returned to later in his career?

14. What was unusual about the player who scored the 50th goal of his career for Velez Sarsfield against Colon in the Argentinian League on 25 August 2000?

15. Which Argentinean club was involved in three World Club Championship matches against Celtic in 1967, winning the trophy after a replay?

EUROPEAN CLUBS – GENERAL

1. Which Englishman was sacked after being manager of Sampdoria for just 48 days in 1999?

2. Who was in charge of Gothenburg when they won the UEFA Cup in 1982?

3. Apart from England, which other country's clubs had won 26 European trophies, prior to the start of the 2000–1 season?

4. Which side has won the Bundesliga on the most occasions?

5. Which side was voted the FIFA Club of the Century in 2001?

6. At the start of the 2000–1 season, which side had played a record 317 matches in the three major European competitions?

7. In 1983–84 who became the only player from an English club to win the European Golden Boot award for most league goals that season?

8. Which Juventus and Italy player was voted European Footballer of the Year in 1993?

9. For which other Dutch club apart from Ajax did Johan Cruyff play in his career?

10. Which club set a new Belgian record by winning their first 14 League matches of the 2000–1 season?

11. Which goalkeeper made a club record 473 appearances for Bayern Munich during his career?

12. What is the name of Real Madrid's second team who played West Ham United in a Cup Winners Cup tie in 1980–81?

13. Which Italian club play at the Stadio Delle Alpi?

14. Which Dynamo Kiev and Russian winger was voted European Footballer of the Year in 1975?

15. Which French side did Real Madrid beat in two European Cup finals in the 1950s?

ENGLAND

1. Whose first goal for his country was in England's 2–0 win over Columbia in the 1998 World Cup?

2. Which was the last country beaten by England in a full international under Kevin Keegan?

3. Against which country in 2000 did Michael Owen score his second goal for England at Wembley?

4. Who was the Watford player who scored a hat-trick for England in the 9–0 rout of Luxembourg at Wembley in 1982?

5. Who was the only player to win 60 caps for England in the 1990s?

6. Which defender in 1988 won his first England cap whilst playing for Middlesbrough in the Second Division?

7. Who with 77 caps for England between 1980–88 is Arsenal's most capped player?

8. Against which country in Italia 90 did Gary Lineker score England's first penalty for four years?

9. Which defender appeared for Sunderland in the 1973 FA Cup final and later won 65 England caps?

10. Which Derby County player nearly scored with his first ever touch for England on his debut against Italy in November 2000?

11. Which Nottingham Forest striker made his only England appearance against the Republic of Ireland in March 1985?

12. Against which country was an England international abandoned in February 1995 due to crowd trouble?

13. Which Premiership keeper won his first cap for England against Mexico at Wembley in 1997?

14. Which Ipswich player scored for England in post-war record six consecutive internationals in 1981–82?

15. Which European country was on the receiving end of England's biggest victory of the 1970s: 7–0 at Wembley in 1973?

BEST OF BRITISH

1. Who was appointed manager of Wales in August 1999?

2. Who scored 12 goals in 59 games for Northern Ireland from 1990–2000 whilst with Luton, Southampton, Crystal Palace, West Ham and QPR?

3. Who was the manager of Scotland from 1978 to 1985 ?

4. Where did Wales play an international for the first time in March 2000 against Finland?

5. Which current manager won 64 caps for Northern Ireland from 1972 to 1985 whilst with Nottingham Forest and Norwich City amongst others?

6. Who scored 30 goals in 55 games for Scotland until retirement after the 1974 World Cup?

7. Who won 59 caps for Wales from 1981 to 1993 whilst with Everton and Cardiff?

8. Which player had a goal disallowed after supposedly kicking the ball out of Gordon Banks's hands in a controversial incident at Windsor Park in 1971?

9. Now a TV pundit, he won eight Scottish caps whilst with Aston Villa and Bayern Munich in 1989 and 1990?

10. Which country defeated Wales 7–1 in a World Cup qualifier in November 1996?

11. Who was the manager of Northern Ireland for four years after being appointed in February 1994?

12. Which country failed to appear for a World Cup qualifier against Scotland in 1996 leading to the memorable 'One team in Tallinn' song by supporters?

13. Which forward player was sent-off for Wales against West Germany in Nuremburg in 1991?

14. Who scored a memorable winning goal for Northern Ireland against West Germany in Hamburg in a European Championship qualifier in 1983?

15. Which Scottish player scored an own goal in their opening World Cup finals match against Brazil in France 1998?

QUICKFIRE

1.   Who scored the winner for Manchester United against Everton in the 1985 FA Cup final and then moved to Goodison Park?

2.   Who captained France when they won the European Championships in 1984?

3.   Which Premiership side beat Tranmere Rovers on penalties in their 1994 League Cup semi-final?

4.   In February 1999 France defeated England 2–0 at Wembley – which then Premiership player scored both goals that night?

5.   Which club in 1998 dropped into the new Second Division for the first time in their history?

6.   Who is the only player to be capped by the Republic of Ireland since the War whose surname begins with the letter 'I'?

7.   Who set a record for the fastest goal in the Premiership in April 1995 when scoring after just 13 seconds of a game for Blackburn Rovers?

8.   From which club did Manchester United sign Jesper Olsen and Liverpool sign Jan Molby?

9.   In 1985–86 who became the first English £1 million player to be given a free transfer when being released by Real Madrid?

10.   Who was the legendary player who coached Panathinaikos to the 1971 European Cup Final?

11.   Which was the first Italian club to win the European Cup?

12.   Which British city provided two clubs in European finals in 1967?

13.   Which club in 1987 became the first to be automatically relegated from the Football League

14.   Who scored a hat-trick for Manchester United in just nine minutes of a match against Aston Villa in the 1984–85 season?

15.   He captained Scotland in the 1970s – even though he was born in England – and later managed Arsenal. Who is he?

QUICKFIRE

1.   Name the Southampton goalkeeper who kept goal for Wales in all eight of their Euro 2000 qualifiers?

2.   Who scored the last ever goal in an international at Wembley?

3.   Which is the only club to defeat Manchester United in a FA Cup final under Sir Alex Ferguson?

4.   With which side was Gary Lineker playing when he was first capped by England in 1984?

5.   Which club is known as 'the Cottagers'?

6.   Whose cancelled transfer from RC Liege to Dunkirk in 1990 had major repercussions for the game?

7.   Who led Liverpool out at Wembley in the 1992 FA Cup final when Graeme Souness was recuperating from heart surgery?

8.   Which club defeated Man Utd by 1–0 to win the 1999–2000 Super Cup?

9.   Which club reached the 1977 and 1984 League Cup finals and lost both after replays?

10.   Bobby Gould resigned as manager of Wales in 1999 after a 4–0 defeat by which country?

11.   Which Division 3 club in 1997–8 became the first side since 1974 to be promoted before the end of March?

12.   Who has made a record 565 appearances for Manchester City in a career from 1959 to 1976?

13.   From which club did Ian Rush move to Liverpool in 1980 for a £300,000 fee?

14.   Who was the teenager who scored for Manchester City in the 1976 League Cup final?

15.   Which player was the leading goalscorer in Division One in 1975–76 with 23 goals whilst with Norwich City?

The Group phase

1. Which three players have scored 30 or more goals in a season in the Premiership?
(3 points)

2. Which five players have scored 40 or more international goals for Germany?
(5 points)

3. Four clubs have appeared in 20 or more FA Cup semi-finals (excluding replays) – who are they?
(4 points)

Penalty Shoot-out

1. Which former Arsenal defender moved to the club from Wimbledon in 1986?

2. Which defender won 58 of his 91 Northern Ireland whilst with Luton Town?

3. Which European country equalled their biggest ever victory when defeating San Marino 10–1 in February 2001?

4. Who was the last English-born manager to win the FA Cup at Wembley?

5. Who scored the 200th league goal of his career for Leicester City against Spurs in 1999?

Full-time

The record for the highest number of penalties saved by a goalkeeper in a career is believed to be held by former Ipswich star Paul Cooper. When making his 56th penalty save, for Man City against Luton in 1989, it meant he had saved more penalties than had been scored against him during his career. In the 1979–80 season he saved eight out of the ten kicks he faced.

'We've been playing an hour and it's just occurred to me that we're drawing 0–0 with a mountain top' – exasperated Scottish radio commentator in a game versus San Marino

A 15–year-old member of a Manchester junior side, the Bangladeshi Northern Eagles, once offered to wash the team's kit. Problem was he used curry powder instead of washing powder. The previously green strip turned yellow

The Group phase

1. Which three German clubs appeared in the Champions League in the 2000–1 season?
   (3 points)

2. Prior to the start of the 2000–1 season there had been seven British player-managers in the Premiership – who?
   (7 points)

3. Which two players appeared in England's first games under Glenn Hoddle, Kevin Keegan and Sven Goran-Eriksson?
   (2 points)

Penalty Shoot-out

1. Who scored both of Holland's goals when they beat the Republic of Ireland in their Euro 96 play-off?

2. Which England international played against Liverpool in the League Cup finals of 1978 and 1987 for Nottingham Forest and Arsenal respectively?

3. Who won eight England caps and all the domestic honours with Manchester City from 1968–70 and saw his son play for City from 1994–97?

4. Who was the Ipswich Town player who scored twice for Scotland in a 5–2 win over New Zealand in the 1982 World Cup?

5. Which player has scored Premiership goals for Arsenal, West Ham, Wimbledon and Coventry City?

Full-time

In 1992–93 Derby County were concerned that an old gypsy curse had caused a bad run of home results. They then called in clairvoyant, Adeline Lee, with impressive results: before the curse was lifted P12 W3 L9 . . . after the curse was lifted P11 W8 D2 L1. In 1992 Gillingham used a priest to lift a curse on the Priestfield stadium which had supposedly hung there since the 1940s following the death of a young gypsy girl in a motor accident involving the manager of the club. They won their next three home games.

Jim Farry, Scottish FA chief executive in 1990: 'We're fed up with people using cliches like "I want players to die for me". That language is more appropriate to a war zone.' Three days later Alex Miller (manager of Hibs): 'If players are not going to die for this club, then I don't want to know them'.

On 28 November 1998 the first meeting between two clubs managed by former England managers took place when Graham Taylor's Watford played Terry Venables' Crystal Palace.

BRITISH CLUBS

1. Of which club is David Mellor a follower?

2. Of which London club was Ron Noades both the chairman and manager?

3. Who made his Manchester United debut aged 17 against Everton in the 1990–1 season?

4. Which Scottish side play at Tynecastle?

5. Which former Nottingham Forest and England defender was appointed as Barnsley's player manager in 1993?

6. Which club has played at Sealand Road, Macclesfield's ground, and now the Deva Stadium?

7. Which North West club used to be known as Newton Heath?

8. Which Scottish league club are actually located in England?

9. Which player has scored for Watford in all four divisions of the Football League?

10. Wimbledon in 1991 set a record fee for a player moving from the Conference to the Football League – who was he?

11. Which Leeds United player was joint leading scorer in the Premiership with 18 goals in the 1998–99 season?

12. Which club did John Beck join as manager in 1992?

13. Which club was managed by Chris Waddle in the 1997–98 season?

14. Which current Division Two side has both Icelandic owners and a manager from that country?

15. Ray Crawford was the Division One leading scorer in 1961–62 season. With which club was he playing?

BRITISH CLUBS

1. Who was the extrovert Carlisle chairman who once claimed he'd seen a UFO and at one time tried to take over Man Utd?

2. Who from 1991–92 to 1996–97 was Arsenal's top scorer in every season?

3. The 'Pirates' played at Eastville, then at Bath City's ground and now inhabit the Memorial Ground – who are they?

4. Which foreign import joined Villa for a club record £3.5 million in 1995 although it was reported Brian Little only saw him on video?

5. Of which club in 1975 did Ray Wilkins become the youngest ever captain aged just 18 years?

6. Which current Premiership club has lost their its six matches at Wembley in all competitions?

7. Which former Chelsea manager won a French League Championship medal?

8. Which Midlands club used to be known as Small Heath?

9. Which club has occupied the top English League division every year since 1919, the longest unbroken run of any top flight English football team?

10. Which flamboyant manager early in his career took Cambridge United up from the Fourth Division to the Second Division from 1974–78?

11. Which club in 1961 became the first to win all three major English trophies?

12. In the 1987 Spurs-Watford FA Cup semi-final, three players with the same surname scored in the game – what was it?

13. Who was the first manager to manage three different English clubs in Europe, Chelsea, QPR and Manchester United?

14. In 1982 which future England centre forward scored four times for Reading in a game they lost 7–5?

15. In 1986–7 Middlesbrough played their first home game of the season at which club's ground, due the financial difficulties?

BIRMINGHAM CITY

1.　Which then 25–year-old became the first female football club managing director in 1992?

2.　Still connected with the club, who was their youngest-ever player aged 16 years seven months in 1970?

3.　The scorer of a winning League Cup final goal, he joined Leicester from Birmingham in 1996 – who is he?

4.　Born in Nigeria, he played in the same Liverpool Boys side as Robbie Fowler, and played against the Liverpool striker in the 2001 League Cup Final – who is he?

5.　From which club did Birmingham pay a record fee of £1.85 million for Jon McCarthy in September 1997?

6.　Who was manager of the club from 1993–96 and signed 41 players in his high profile spell at his club?

7.　Which club defeated Birmingham 7–6 on penalties in the 1999 play-off semi-finals?

8.　Who scored Wembley's first golden goal in the 1995 Windscreens final that gave Birmingham a win over Carlisle?

9.　Who, having played in the 1978 World Cup Final, made his League debut for Birmingham at Tottenham, who were fielding his international team-mate Osvaldo Ardiles?

10.　Which former Leeds defender was sacked by Birmingham a mere 16 days into the 1977–8 season?

11.　Who in February 1974 left St Andrews for a record £350,000 and went on to win 12 England caps with Everton?

12.　Later to play for Watford and Manchester City, who saved a penalty after 80 seconds of his Football League debut against Sunderland on 27 December 1980?

13.　Whilst in Division Two in 1971–2 the club lost just once in 23 games after New Year's Day. Which club defeated them 3–0 in the FA Cup semi-final?

14.　Birmingham in 2001 reached their first League Cup final since 1963, when they beat which side 3–1 on aggregate?

15.　Which was the last side to meet Birmingham in a FA Cup final?

ASTON VILLA

1.   Which ex-Villa player scored for England at Villa Park
     against Spain in February 2000?

2.   Which player did the club sell for a record £12.6 million
     in August 1998?

3.   Villa has been managed by only one overseas coach. Who?

4.   Who kept goal for Villa in both of the club's League Cup
     final wins in 1994 and 1996?

5.   Villa reached the League Cup semi-final in 1999–2000
     but lost 1–0 on aggregate to which club?

6.   Which club did Villa defeat to win their last trophy at
     Wembley?

7.   Who was the Welsh international in Villa's FA Cup final
     side in 2000?

8.   Which club did Villa defeat on penalties in the FA Cup
     semi-final in 2000?

9.   Which World Cup player in 1990 had just been voted the
     PFA Player of the Year with Villa?

10. Who left Man Utd and then won the PFA Player of the
     Year with Villa in 1993?

11. Which defender scored all four goals in Villa's game
     against Leicester City in 1976 – two for Villa and two own
     goals?

12. Who was the manager when Villa last won the league in
     1981, using just 14 players in the process?

13. Which player scored a spectacular goal at Goodison Park
     in 1981 which was voted goal of the season?

14. In five seasons, 1977–82 inclusive, which goalkeeper
     missed only one league game for Villa?

15. Who between August 1979 to May 1983 played in a
     record 215 successive first-team games, which ended with
     a broken leg sustained in a pre-season tournament in
     1983?

THE CUPS – GENERAL

1. Which club appeared in four FA Cup finals from 1986–92?

2. Who was the manager of Sunderland when they won the FA Cup in 1973?

3. Which side defeated Manchester United 3–0 in the FA Charity Shield in August 1998?

4. Who managed Liverpool when they won the League Cup in 1995?

5. Which was the last side to concede four goals in a Wembley FA Cup final?

6. Which side lost in the FA Charity Shield to both Manchester United in 1994 and Everton in 1995?

7. Which player scored for Spurs in the 1991 FA Cup final but moved to Liverpool 12 months later?

8. In the 1985 League Cup final which Sunderland player missed a penalty when shooting against the base of the post?

9. Who scored a rare Wembley hat-trick for Chelsea when they beat Manchester City 5–4 in the 1986 Full Members' Cup final at Wembley?

10. Who scored for Sheffield Wednesday in both the 1993 FA Cup semi-final and final at Wembley?

11. Who scored a hat-trick for Leeds when they beat Liverpool 4–3 in the 1992 Charity Shield, the last one scored in the match at Wembley?

12. Which side won the FA Cup three times during the 1960s?

13. Which Premiership side last won the FA Cup in 1957?

14. Which club's victory in the 2000 Auto Windscreens Shield final at Wembley was dedicated to the late Sir Stanley Matthews?

15. Which famous club played their last FA Cup tie on 25 November 1961 before leaving the league?

FA CUP – The 90s

1. Who came on as a substitute for Crystal Palace and scored twice against Manchester United in the 1990 final?
2. And who was the Crystal Palace manager in that game who at 34 was the second youngest manager in Wembley history?
3. Which club appeared in an FA Cup final during the decade in the same season as they were relegated from the English top flight?
4. Who was the England international who lifted the FA Cup for Liverpool in 1992?
5. Who was the only forward to captain a Cup-winning side during the decade?
6. Which England international became the first player to appear against both North London rivals in the Cup final, playing against Spurs in 1991 and Arsenal in 1998?
7. Who scored Manchester United's last gasp equaliser against Oldham at Wembley in their 1994 semi-final?
8. Which side ended Manchester United's hopes of reaching four consecutive FA Cup finals by defeating them 1–0 in a Fourth Round replay in 1996–97?
9. Which First Division side were beaten 2–0 by Chelsea in the FA Cup semi-final at Wembley in 1994?
10. Which goalkeeper did Alex Ferguson drop after the first game of the 1990 FA Cup final?
11. Who was the only man to manage two different clubs in FA Cup finals during the decade?
12. Who scored his 42nd goal in the FA Cup during the decade to surpass Denis Law's record for most FA Cup goals in the 20th century?
13. In 1991–92 which ground staged FA cup-ties on consecutive days in the third round when Farnborough played West Ham, followed the next day by Charlton against Orient?
14. Who, when coming on for Everton in the 1995 and Newcastle in 1999 became the first man to appear as a substitute for different clubs in FA Cup finals?
15. Which player scored for Sunderland in every round bar the final in 1992?

SPANISH CLUBS

1. At what stadium do Real Madrid play their home games?

2. Who managed Barcelona to their first Spanish title in eleven years in 1985?

3. Which club won the Spanish title for the first time in 2000?

4. Who were the brothers who moved from Ajax to Barcelona for a combined fee of £14,000,000 in January 1999?

5. And who moved for a then-world record fee of £922,000 from Ajax to Barcelona in the summer of 1973?

6. Which famous player scored a club record of 218 league goals for Real Madrid from 1953–64?

7. For which club does Spanish international star Gaizka Mendieta play in the Primera Liga?

8. Which player moved from Deportivo La Coruna to Barcelona in August 1997 for £12.5 million?

9. Which Real Madrid striker of the 1980s and 1990s was nicknamed 'the Vulture'?

10. Which club last won the Spanish title in 1984 when they also lost to Liverpool in the European Cup?

11. Which German international played for Real Madrid, Atletico Madrid and Barcelona in the 1980s?

12. Which club did Real Madrid beat in the European Cup semi-finals in 1999–2000 despite losing 4–1 and 4–2 to the same side in the earlier group stages?

13. From 1985–98 this goalkeeper won a record number of caps for Spain and also holds the record for most appearances in the Primera Liga with 622 in his career?

14. What is the name of the second club in Barcelona, whose ground was used for the famous Italy-Brazil clash in the 1982 World Cup?

15. Which Brazilian star was the leading goalscorer in the Primera Liga with 30 goals for Barcelona in 1993–94?

ITALIAN CLUBS

1. Which club did Sven-Goran Eriksson manage to the Serie A title in 2000?

2. In which city is the San Siro stadium?

3. Which club is nicknamed 'the Grand Old Lady of Italian football'?

4. Which overseas star scored 129 goals for Fiorentina in Serie A before moving to Roma in the summer of 2000?

5. Which club did Diego Maradona lead to the Italian title for the only two occasions in their history in 1987 and 1990?

6. Which club remained unbeaten in Serie A during 1991–92 in winning the title by eight points?

7. Who was the Italian international striker who began his career by being the leading scorer in Serie A with 24 goals with Vicenza in 1977–78?

8. Which Italian World Cup-winning captain made a record 570 appearances in Serie A?

9. Who was the Argentinian striker who moved from Parma to Roma in the summer of 2000 for £35 million?

10. In which city do Sampdoria play their home matches?

11. Who was the manager of the great AC Milan side of the late 1980s who resigned after just three games in charge of Parma in 2001?

12. Which club did German internationals Lothar Matthaus and Andreas Brehme help to the Serie A title in 1989?

13. Which famous international was the leading goalscorer in Serie A with Juventus for three consecutive seasons from 1982–5?

14. Which Italian side did Graeme Souness manage for just six matches in the 1997–98 season?

15. Which Italian club won three major European trophies in the 1990s having won just two domestic honours in their history?

EURO 2000

1. Which of the host countries opened the tournament with a 2–1 win over Sweden?

2. Who scored England's second goal when they lost 3–2 to Portugal in their opening group match?

3. Which former Premiership player scored five goals for Yugoslavia in the competition?

4. Who said after the tournament: 'I wouldn't say I've set the world alight with my managerial skills'?

5. Who qualified for the knock-out stages only after scoring two extra-time goals to beat Yugoslavia 4–3?

6. Which side defeated both of the host countries during the tournament?

7. Who scored the winning goal for France in extra-time in the final against Italy?

8. In their quarter-final against France which Spanish player missed a late penalty in a match they lost 2–1?

9. Holland recorded the biggest victory of the competition, by 6–1 against which country?

10. Who was sent-off in the Romania-Italy quarter-final after being sent-off for Galatasaray against Arsenal in the 2000 UEFA Cup Final?

11. Who was the manager of Holland who resigned after the competition?

12. Which England player was substituted in all three of his side's matches?

13. Which Leicester City player made his international debut during the competition?

14. In which city did England play both Romania and Germany?

15. Who scored a hat-trick for Portugal against Germany in the group stages?

EURO 96

1. Against which country did England win their quarter-final match on penalties?

2. Who scored Scotland's only goal of the tournament against Switzerland?

3. Which country did France knock out on penalties in a quarter-final tie?

4. Whose three goals in the finals for Croatia enabled him to equal the record of 16 goals scored in European Championship football?

5. Which country did Germany play twice in the finals?

6. Who captained Scotland during the tournament?

7. Whose consolation goal for Holland in the 4–1 defeat by England kept them in the tournament?

8. Apart from David Seaman and Tim Flowers who was the other goalkeeper included in England's squad?

9. Which country qualified for the finals for the first time but then lost 2–1 to Germany in the knock-out stages?

10. Which Bulgarian player scored in all of his sides three group matches?

11. Which country played England in the opening game of the tournament?

12. Who scored the crucial winning penalty for Germany in their shoot-out triumph over England?

13. Which ground staged the semi-final between France and the Czech Republic?

14. Which former West Ham player scored Romania's only goal of the tournament against Spain?

15. Which country failed to score a point or a goal in the tournament?

QUICKFIRE

1. On whose head did The Sun superimpose a picture of a turnip after a defeat and used the headlines: 'Swedes 2 Turnips 1'?

2. Which current Arsenal player was the first to appear for England who was born after the 1966 World Cup win?

3. With which club did Bobby Moore make his last appearance at Wembley, doing so in 1975?

4. For which club did Gary Lineker play in Japan before retirement?

5. Which TV pundit moved from Brighton to Liverpool for a £900,000 fee in 1981?

6. What is the name given to the Swan who is the mascot of Swansea?

7. Whose last game for Scotland was the 1978 World Cup defeat by Peru in which he missed a penalty?

8. Ian Wright and David Platt both scored four times for England against the same country – who was it?

9. Which club in 1983–4 became the first to score 100 points doing so in Division Four?

10. Which club in 1990 won a Wembley play-off, but due to financial irregularities, did not gain promotion?

11. Which then-Ajax midfielder was sent home from Euro '96 after making disparaging remarks about coach Gus Heedink?

12. Which goalkeeper made his 600th league appearance for Chelsea in May 1979?

13. Which club made its first Wembley appearance against Ipswich in the 2000 Division One play-off final?

14. When Spurs beat Everton 10–4 in the highest scoring post-war league match, which manager was taking charge of the victors for the first time?

15. Norman Whiteside broke which West Ham player's record set in 1964 for the youngest FA Cup final goalscorer at Wembley?

QUICKFIRE

1. Who was the Everton defender who won his first England cap against Spain in February 2001?

2. Which club's mascot is called 'Harry the Hornet'?

3. Which club did Danny Wilson take to the Premiership from Division One in 1997 only to be immediately relegated?

4. Who captained Germany to victory in the final of Euro 96?

5. Which club came within two minutes of winning the 1999 European Champions Cup?

6. Who coached England during the 1996 European Championships?

7. Which former Coventry City player set a new USA appearance record when winning his 129th cap in 2000?

8. Whose appearance for Burnley against Wigan in February 2000 led to an attendance of 20,345 to Turf Moor?

9. Which goalkeeper played his 1000th senior game against Norwich City in February 1983?

10. Which England international made his 600th appearance for Leeds United in 1972?

11. Which club has one of the highest capacities for any single stand in Europe, their Holte End seating over 13,000?

12. Kevin Davies was the youngest player to appear in a League Cup game in October 1993 aged only 16 years and 104 days. Which club was he playing for?

13. Which Dutchman retired from international football just before the 1994 World Cup aged just 32?

14. Who started his career with Everton and played in both the 1988 and 1989 FA Cup finals for Liverpool?

15. England played Portugal in the 1966 World Cup semi-finals. Which country did West Germany defeat at that stage?

The Group phase

1. Which four clubs have won all three major European
    trophies?
    (4 points)

2. Since 1988 six managers have won the FA Cup with clubs
    that they had played for earlier in the career –who are
    they?
    (6 points)

3. Which two English sides play at grounds called St James
    Park?
    (2 points)

Penalty Shoot-out

1. Which man managed both Aston Villa and Celtic during
    the 1990s?

2. During the 2000–1 season who became the most
    expensive player ever purchased by a Scottish club, when
    costing £12 million?

3. Who kept an incredible 35 clean sheets in 73 England
    appearances from 1963 to 1972?

4. Who is the most capped Romanian player of all time?

5. Which club appeared in the League Cup final on three
    occasions between 1966 and 1970?

Full-time

When Arsenal played Chelsea in the Premiership in May 2000, for the first time in over 30 years an English league game featured five players with World Cup winners' medals: Desailly, Deschamps and Leboeuf for Chelsea with Petit and Viera for Arsenal. The last instance had been Manchester United and West Ham in the years after 1966.

Hartlepool chairman Garry Gibson on his club's debt: 'The listening bank refused to listen and the bank that likes to say yes, said no.'

Robert Prytz appeared for Malmo against Nottingham Forest in the 1979 European Cup final. When the teams next met, in the UEFA Cup 17 years later, he again played for the Swedes.

The Group phase

1. During the 1990s against which six countries did England lose internationals at Wembley?
    (6 points)

2. Which three Manchester United players won the PFA Young Player of the Year award in the 1990s?
    (3 points)

3. Who are the last three Englishmen to have managed a league title-winning side in England?
    (3 points)

Penalty Shoot-out

1. Against which country did Pat Jennings make his final appearance for Northern Ireland in the 1986 World Cup on his 41st birthday?

2. Which current Premiership manager was Scotland's only scorer in the 1986 World Cup finals?

3. Which player famously scored six times for Manchester City in a FA Cup tie in 1961 against Luton Town only to see the match abandoned?

4. Who overtook Bobby Charlton as England's most capped player in 1973?

5. What was the surname of the brothers who were managers of the opposing sides in the 1991 Scottish FA Cup final when Dundee United played Motherwell?

Full-time

The wife of Claudio Caniggia agreed to his return to Argentina in 1997 only on the condition he celebrated goals without kissing and hugging. She was not too pleased therefore when he and close friend Diego Maradona celebrated goals for Boca Juniors by kissing each other on the lips!

Terry Venables on Paul Gascoigne signing for Lazio: 'It's a bit like seeing you're mother-in-law drive over a cliff in your new car'.

The term 'derby match' is believed to have come from the annual football matches played between the parishes of St Peter's and All Saints in Derby.

BRITISH CLUBS

1. Who was the former Liverpool goalkeeper who at the age of 42 played for Northwich Victoria in the FA Cup in 1999–2000?

2. Which player did Arsenal sign from Paris St Germain for £500,000 in the summer of 1997?

3. Which striker did Leeds United sign for £2 million in 1997 who was then bought by another side three years later for £15 million?

4. Who was the first player-manager to win the League Championship in England?

5. Which Scottish city's two league grounds are only 100 yards apart?

6. Which Frenchman scored a first-half hat-trick in the Arsenal-West Ham game at Highbury in March 2001?

7. Which club ended Leeds United's ten-game winning run with a last-minute equaliser in a 4–4 draw in October 1999?

8. Which club did Ally McCoist join after leaving Rangers?

9. Derek Clarke was the first substitute in a FA Cup final in 1968, but for which side?

10. Who was the Newcastle United striker fined £10,000 and banned for the opening match of the 1996–97 season for striking Keith Curle of Manchester City in February 1996?

11. Later to move to Leeds, in 1997 he scored the last-minute winner for Crystal Palace against Sheffield United in the First Division play-off – who was he?

12. Which QPR striker, with Italian roots, moved to Sampdoria in March 1997?

13. Which player was on the losing sides in the FA Cup final for Preston in 1937 and Liverpool in 1950?

14. In 1997 Celtic sacked their manager after a second trophy-less season – who was he?

15. Which club won the FA Cup in 1948 by defeating First Division clubs in every round?

BRITISH CLUBS

1. Who replaced Kevin Keegan as manager of Newcastle United in 1997?

2. Which famous player moved from Torino to Manchester United for £115,000 in July 1962?

3. Who scored 357 league goals in a career – all in Division One – for Chelsea, Spurs and West Ham?

4. Who are the 'Tigers' who play at Boothferry Park?

5. Who was the England winger who had a loan spell from Real Madrid to Manchester United in 1983?

6. Sven Goran Eriksson rejected a chance to join which North West club as manager in 1996–7?

7. Which club sold Gordon Cowans and Paul Rideout to Bari in 1984–85?

8. Who scored Arsenal's last minute winner against Manchester United in the 1979 FA Cup Final?

9. Which defender moved from Leeds United to Manchester United for £495,000 in February 1978?

10. Now Harry Redknapp's deputy at West Ham, he scored a last-minute goal for the 'Hammers' against Everton in an FA Cup semi-final – who is he?

11. Which Liverpool player was due to join Leeds United in December 1996 but changed his mind at the last minute and joined Spurs?

12. Later to join Manchester United in 1980 he played against them – as Southampton's youngest-ever player – aged 16 years 313 days. Who is he?

13. For which club did Mick Quinn score four times on his debut on the opening day of the 1989–90 season against Leeds United?

14. Which English club played in the World Club Championship in 1982?

15. Which Manchester City player in 1969 became only the second uncapped player to be voted Football Writers' Player of the Year?

BLACKBURN ROVERS

1. Who managed the club when they won the Premiership title in 1995?

2. And who was the chairman whose financial backing helped Blackburn win the trophy?

3. Which member of Blackburn's Premiership-winning side went on to win a Scottish title with Rangers?

4. In November 1993 which Blackburn signing became the first £2 million goalkeeper in British football?

5. In November 1991 who became Rovers' first £1 million signing under Kenny Dalglish, moving from Everton?

6. Which player scored a club record 168 league goals between 1978 and 1992?

7. Who captained the club to the title in 1995 before moving to a London club in 1999?

8. Who was the winger who won his first England cap with Blackburn in 1996 against Hungary before joining Leeds United?

9. Which future member of the England backroom staff made a club record 596 league appearances from 1970–1986?

10. Who was the Rovers player dismissed after just 72 seconds of a Premiership match against Leeds United in 1995?

11. Who scored the goal that gave Rovers their win at Anfield in the FA Cup in 1999–2000?

12. For which player did the club pay a club record £7.25 million in June 1998?

13. In 1992 Blackburn were the first club to hit seven goals in a Premiership game, which side did they beat 7–1?

14. Who was Blackburn's captain in the 1960 FA Cup final who also captained England?

15. Who moved for a fee of £3.4 million from Derby to Blackburn in March 1999?

BOLTON WANDERERS

1. What was the name of the ground used by the club before they moved to the Reebok Stadium?

2. Who top-scored for Bolton in the 1999–2000 season before moving to Chelsea?

3. What nationality is Bolton defender Mark Fish?

4. Which Republic of Ireland international left the club for Liverpool in 1995 for £4.5 million?

5. Which fellow Division One side defeated Bolton in the 1999–2000 League Cup semi-finals?

6. Which Scottish striker was the leading scorer in Division One with Bolton in both the 1993–94 and 1996–97 seasons?

7. Who won eight league titles as a player with Liverpool from 1976 to 1986 and then managed Bolton from 1985 to 1992?

8. Which fellow North West club did Bolton play in an emotional FA Cup final in 1958?

9. Which much-travelled striker was the First Division's leading scorer in the 1978–9 season with 24 goals, including a memorable strike for Bolton against Ipswich?

10. Which legendary player scored 255 league goals for the club from 1946 to 1961 and later became Club President?

11. Which current Premiership manager started his playing career with Bolton in the 1970s?

12. In the 1992–93 season who scored 33 goals for the club before moving to Celtic?

13. Which player has scored three times against Bolton in a FA Cup final?

14. Which England international goalkeeper made 519 league appearances for the club from 1956 to 1970?

15. Who managed the club from 1974 to 1980, including promotion to the top flight in 1978?

THE CUPS – GENERAL

1. In 2001 who became the first club to defeat Manchester United in the FA Cup since Barnsley in 1998?

2. Who was the manager of Second Division Oldham Athletic when they played in the 1990 League Cup final?

3. Which club played in the Charity Shield at Wembley for the only time when losing to Liverpool in 1988?

4. Who in 1990 and 1993 became the second player to score in FA Cup finals at Wembley for different clubs?

5. Who when playing for Leicester City in 1969 became the youngest goalkeeper to appear in the final?

6. Who was the captain of Manchester United in their three FA Cup Final wins at Wembley in 1983, 1985 and 1990?

7. What trophy replaced the Simod Cup in 1990, the first winners being Chelsea?

8. Who made 84 appearances in the FA Cup – 80 for Manchester United and four for Preston North End?

9. Which player appeared in the 1990 League Cup final for Oldham and the 1994 final for Aston Villa?

10. Who led Leeds United out in the 1974 Charity Shield at Wembley during a controversial 44 days in charge at the club?

11. The third round in 1962–63 saw Spurs lose an FA Cup tie for the first time in three years against which side, whom they had beaten 3–1 in the previous year's final?

12. Who were the first sponsors of the League Cup in 1982?

13. Who was the Tranmere Rovers player sent-off in the 2000 League Cup final against Leicester City?

14. Which club inflicted Liverpool's first defeat in a League Cup tie since 1980, by 1–0 in October 1984?

15. In the 1965–66 season which player scored 21 goals in the FA Cup, League Cup and World Cup finals?

FA CUP – THE 1980s

1. Which club appeared in three consecutive finals during the decade?

2. Who managed the winners in 1986 and 1989?

3. Who scored twice for Liverpool in FA Cup semi-finals against Nottingham Forest in both 1988 and 1989?

4. Which club suffered their first FA Cup final defeat in their eighth final during the decade?

5. Who when playing for Man United in 1985 became the first Dane to appear in the final?

6. In 1988 who became the first player to miss a penalty in the final at Wembley?

7. In 1981 which club were prevented from reaching a fourth consecutive final when losing to Everton 2–0 in the third round?

8. Which club reached their only semi-final during the decade when losing 3–2 to Coventry in 1987?

9. Which man appeared for Manchester City in the 1981 Final and Coventry in the 1987 Final?

10. When Tottenham beat Manchester United 1–0 at Old Trafford in a 1980 third round replay which England international outfielder replaced the injured Milija Aleksic in goal?

11. Which side lost 4–1 to Spurs in their 1987 FA Cup semi-final, the biggest semi-final defeat of the decade?

12. Who managed the 1980 winners West Ham?

13. During the decade, which became the first club to win the FA Cup with a side consisting of non-English players?

14. Who was the referee who sent off Kevin Moran in the 1985 final?

15. Later to win a league Championship medal with Everton, he captained Man City in the 1981 final – who is he?

EUROPEAN CLUBS – General

1. At which stadium do Barcelona play their home matches?

2. Who managed in the Premiership from 1998–2000 and won all three European trophies as a player?

3. Which legendary goalkeeper was the first Russian to be voted European Footballer of the Year in 1963?

4. In 1987 who became the most expensive player in history when moving from PSV Eindhoven to AC Milan?

5. Which Scottish side won the European Super Cup in 1983 by defeating Hamburg 2–0 on aggregate?

6. Which European side won the World Club Championship in both 1989 and 1990?

7. Which club has won the Belgian title on a record 25 occasions?

8. In 1996 who became only the second French side to win a European trophy, when winning the Cup Winners Cup final?

9. Which German side have played over 160 matches in Europe, yet have played in only one final, when losing in the UEFA Cup final in 1986?

10. Which club has won the Swedish title on a record 18 occasions?

11. Which side did Valencia beat 5–3 on aggregate in the semi-finals of the European Cup in 1999–2000?

12. Which Yugoslavian international scored the only goal of the 1998 European Cup final to give Real Madrid the trophy?

13. What famous ground is officially known as the Guiseppe Meazza stadium?

14. Later to play for Liverpool, he moved from Werder Bremen to Lazio in 1990 for £5.5 million?

15. MTK and Vasas are clubs in which European capital city?

BRITISH CLUBS IN EUROPE

1. When Liverpool won the European Super Cup in 1977 against Hamburg, which of their former players was in the German side?

2. Who captained Chelsea to victory in the Cup Winners Cup final in 1998?

3. For which English side did Bobby Moncur score in both legs of a UEFA Cup final?

4. Which Liverpool goalkeeper's 'wobbly legs' in the 1984 European Cup final resulted in two Roma players missing in the penalty shoot-out?

5. Which Danish player scored the winner for Chelsea against FC Copenhagen in the Cup Winners Cup in 1998 and then joined the Danish club four days later?

6. Real Zaragoza defeated Arsenal in the 1995 European Cup Winners Cup final, but which other English side did they defeat in the semi-final?

7. Playing in Division One in the 2000–1 season, they played their only season in Europe in 1983–84 after finishing runners-up to Liverpool the previous year?

8. Which current Premiership side has played in Europe on five occasions, four of them in Cup Winners Cup?

9. Who was the Spurs goalkeeper whose penalty shoot-out heroics in the final won them the UEFA Cup in 1984?

10. Which midfield player scored Newcastle United's first ever European hat-trick against Antwerp in 1994?

11. Who won a Cup Winners Cup winner's medal with Manchester City in 1970 and then a European Cup winner's medal with Nottingham Forest in 1979 and 1980?

12. Whose missed penalty for Arsenal in the 1980 Cup Winners Cup final saw Valencia win the trophy?

13. Rangers won the 1972 Cup Winners Cup by defeating which Russian side 3–2 in the final?

14. Which club, who play in Division One, were England's representatives in the European Cup in the 1960–61 season when they lost to Hamburg in the quarter-final?

15. Which substitute's memorable diving header in extra-time scored the winning goal for Aberdeen in the 1983 Cup Winners Cup final?

EUROPEAN CHAMPIONSHIPS – General

1. Whose memorable volley secured a 2–0 victory for Holland in the 1988 European Championship Final?

2. Which future Premiership player scored for Denmark when they won the Final of Euro 92 in Sweden?

3. Which member of France's winning team in 1984 is currently a manager in English football?

4. Which country was beaten in the European Championship Finals of 1972 and 1988?

5. When Germany won the trophy in 1972 who scored twice in the final?

6. Who scored a record nine goals in five games for France when they won the trophy on their own soil in 1984?

7. England lost one game in the 1980 finals, to which country 1–0 in a group match?

8. Which country were the second winners of the competition in 1964?

9. Who scored for Manchester United in an FA Cup final and played in the 1988 European Championship final for Holland aged 38 years?

10. When Denmark won the trophy in 1992 which country did they defeat on penalties in the semi-final?

11. Which country did France beat 3–2 in a memorable semi-final in Marseilles in 1984?

12. Which country were beaten 12–1 by Spain in a qualifying match in 1983, the biggest defeat in the competition's history?

13. In the 1976 final, which German player missed the crucial penalty in the shoot-out that gave the title to Czechoslovakia?

14. Two players appeared for Denmark in the 1992 final who also played for Manchester United in their career, Peter Schmeichel and which former United full back?

15. Which Hamburg striker scored both of West Germany's goals in the 1980 final against Belgium?

ENGLAND

1. Which player scored for England in both their opening games of France '98 and Euro 2000?

2. Which Premiership player scored the winning goal for Romania against England in their first round group match in France '98?

3. Against which country did England suffer their only defeat under Terry Venables in open play, 3–1 at Wembley in June 1995?

4. Which current Chelsea player scored on his international debut against Turkey in 1991?

5. Whose hat-trick against England in the 1988 European Championships was in Peter Shilton's 100th game for his country?

6. Who was the only outfield player to be capped by England in each of the last three decades: the 1980, 1990s and 2000?

7. Which Third Division player scored for England on his international debut at Hampden Park in 1989?

8. Who scored England's only goal of the 1992 European Championships, doing so against the hosts Sweden?

9. Two Sunderland players made their international debuts for England against Hungary in April 1999, Kevin Phillips and who else?

10. Who, with 21 goals in 46 games, was England's leading goalscorer of the 1970s?

11. While with which Italian club were both Trevor Francis and David Platt capped for England?

12. Who captained England for the first time against Italy in November 2000?

13. Which South American country inflicted England's first defeat at Wembley for six years in 1990?

14. Whose only goal in 35 England internationals was scored during the 1970 World Cup finals against West Germany?

15. Which Asian country did England face for the first time in May 1996, in a warm up game for Euro 96, England winning 3–0?

QUICKFIRE

1.   Which current Liverpool player made his international
     debut in September 1995 against Colombia whilst with
     Middlesbrough?

2.   In which year was the World Cup Final held at the Rose
     Bowl?

3.   With which club do you associate Mohammed Al Fayed?

4.   Which Newcastle manager was the first to leave a
     Premiership club during the 1999–2000 season, doing so
     in September 1999?

5.   Jeff Astle and Tony Brown were the leading scorers in
     Division One in the 1969–70 and 1970–71 seasons with
     the same club, which one?

6.   Which man from Switzerland preceded George Graham as
     manager of Spurs?

7.   Which country knocked the Republic of Ireland out of
     Italia 90 in the quarter-finals?

8.   In 1995 which former England striker left Glasgow
     Rangers for Queens Park Rangers?

9.   Which Portuguese side won the World Club Championship
     in 1987?

10. Which club, formerly known as Headington, won their
     only major trophy, the League Cup, in the 1980s?

11. Which club, former league champions of England, won
     the Fourth Division and Third Division titles in
     consecutive seasons in 1987–88 and 1988–89?

12. Who was the famous Polish goalkeeper – nicknamed 'The
     Clown' by Brian Clough – in their 1973 World Cup
     qualifier against England at Wembley?

13. Which current Premiership player was unable to captain
     Scotland in the 1998 World Cup finals due to injury, and
     later retired from international football?

14. In 1990 rival clubs from which city were promoted from
     the old Division Three to Division Two?

15. Which was the first country to produce three different
     clubs as winners of the European Cup?

QUICKFIRE

1. With which club do you associate Martin Edwards as chairman?

2. Which famous player was included in the Northern Ireland World Cup squad in 1982 whilst playing for the San Jose Earthquakes?

3. Who played for Brazil in four World Cup final stages from 1958 to 1970?

4. Later to become Welsh manager in 1992–93 he managed Coventry City in the Premiership – who is he?

5. For which Scottish club did Willie Miller make a record 556 appearances from 1973 to 1990?

6. Gary Lineker was playing for which side when they were knocked out of the FA Cup in 1980 by non-league Harlow?

7. From which club was Les Sealey on loan when he played for Manchester United in the 1990 FA Cup finals?

8. In 1995 who equalled a club record by scoring in his eighth consecutive game for Newcastle United?

9. Which former Chelsea player took over as manager of Barnsley in the 2000–1 season after previously managing Sheffield United?

10. In 1964 which was the last Welsh club to reach the FA Cup semi-finals?

11. Now working as a TV pundit, this Republic of Ireland international helped Liverpool to the Double in 1986 and Leeds to the Division Two title in 1990 – who is he?

12. Which British side was the first country to be eliminated from the World Cup finals without losing a game?

13. Who was congratulated for his sporting conduct when he asked the referee not to award a penalty, after being brought down by David Seaman, in a league match at Highbury in 1997?

14. Which Rosenborg striker did Spurs buy in 1996 for a fee of £2.7 million?

15. Which Watford player in 1997 became the youngest to score a hat-trick for the Republic of Ireland, when scoring three against Leichtenstein?

The Group phase

1. Since Kenny Dalglish left in 1995 which five men have managed Blackburn Rovers?
    (5 points)

2. Which two teams reaching the European Cup quarter-finals in 2000–1 were not from England or Spain?
    (2 points)

3. With which five clubs was Ian Dowie capped for Northern Ireland during his career?
    (5 points)

Penalty Shoot-out

1. In 2000 which former Premiership player made his record 101st appearance for France?

2. When Kevin Keegan came on as substitute for England against Spain in the 1982 World Cup, which other player came on with him for his only appearance of the tournament?

3. Chris Hutchings was the manager of which Premiership club at the start of the 2000–1 season?

4. Which Manchester United player was sent-off after the final whistle against Galatasaray in Turkey in a European Cup tie in 1993?

5. With which club was Lee Hughes the leading scorer in Division One in the 1998–99 season?

Full-time

Every schoolboy knows that the highest score in British football is when Arbroath beat Bon Accord 36–0 in the Scottish Cup on 12 September 1885. Less well known is that on the same day, in the same competition, Dundee Harp beat Aberdeen Rovers 35–0!

'I looked more like Val Doonican than Valderrama' – Andy Townsend after dying his hair in the 1994 World Cup.

The only two goalkeepers to save penalties in Wembley FA Cup finals, Dave Beasant and Mark Crossley, were later team-mates at Nottingham Forest in the late 1990s. Crossley, incidentally, remains the only goalkeeper to save one of the 49 penalties taken in first-team matches by Matthew Le Tissier.

The Group phase

1. Who are the last four Englishman to score in a FA Cup
    final prior to 2001?
    (4 points)

2. Which four countries have Scotland beaten in the final
    stages of the World Cup?
    (4 points)

3. Which four members of Derby County's League
    Championship winning sides of the 1970s later went on to
    manage Bolton Wanderers?
    (4 points)

Penalty Shoot-out

1. Which Leeds United player was voted PFA Young player
    of the Year in 2000?

2. Which man won the Scottish Manager of the Year award
    five times in the 1990s?

3. Which was the first country to stage the World Cup finals
    on two occasions?

4. Against which country did Howard Wilkinson take charge
    of England for a second time in 2000?

5. Prior to France, which had been the only other country to
    hold the World Cup and European Championship trophies
    simultaneously?

Full-time

The greatest number of games in international football without a victory is the 67 played by Luxembourg between 1980 and 1992; included in this run were 32 consecutive defeats.

'There are 11 men sitting on yellow cards and that's an uncomfortable position to be in' – John Motson at the World Cup

On 20 February 1993 two Australians kept goal in an English league game for the first time when Mark Bosnich of Aston Villa and Jason Kearton of Everton were in opposition. The next day two Czechoslovakians kept goal in a league game for the first time when Ludek Miklosko (West Ham) faced Pavel Srnicek (Newcastle).

BRITISH CLUBS

1. Of which club is the 'punk' violinist Nigel Kennedy a fan?

2. Which Midlands club, in the Premiership for the 2000–1 season, has been in the top flight since promotion in 1967?

3. Which Spurs international is unfortunately nicknamed 'Sicknote' because of his habit of picking up injuries?

4. Which current First Division club won the FA Amateur Cup in 1963 and since then has also won the FA Cup?

5. Who was the Scottish full-back who won the FA Cup with Manchester United in 1977, 1983 and 1985?

6. In which town do Port Vale play their home games?

7. Which club in the 1990s fielded three Spanish players in their line-up: Isidro Diaz, Roberto Martinez and Jesus Saba?

8. Guiliano Grazioli scored five goals for the club nicknamed 'the Posh' in a league match against Barnet in 1998–9. Who are they?

9. Who played in over 650 league games for Tottenham from 1969 to 1986?

10. Which North West club did Tommy Docherty, Bill Shankly and Howard Kendall all play for?

11. Which club started the 1960–1 season by winning their first 11 games in the First Division?

12. Which club's most capped player is Alan McDonald who won 52 Northern Ireland caps?

13. Which was the first side to win the League Cup in successive seasons?

14. Who was the last player to score an own goal in a FA Cup final at Wembley?

15. Which club's former ground is represented in L.S. Lowry's famous painting 'Going to the Match'?

BRITISH CLUBS

1. Malcolm Allison started his managerial league career at
    Home Park in the1960s – which club play there?

2. Which club did Paul Merson play for between his time at
    Arsenal and Aston Villa?

3. Which man had three separate spells in charge of Crystal
    Palace during the 1990s?

4. Which Englishman, who retired from international
    football in the 2000–1 season, played more matches at
    Wembley than any other player?

5. On which club's ground did England beat Spain 3–0 in
    Sven Goran Eriksson's first game in charge?

6. Who left Southend for Nottingham Forest for a record
    £2million in 1993?

7. Which club learned that they'd won the League
    Championship in 1972 whilst sunning themselves on a
    beach in Majorca?

8. Based at Gay Meadow, this club has won the Welsh Cup
    six times, the first in 1891 and the latest in 1985 – who
    are they?

9. Which club became the first to win the League and
    League Cup in the same season, doing so in 1978?

10. Which of the game's characters netted 44 goals when QPR
    won the Third Division and League Cup in 1966–67?

11. Why should Doncaster manager Sammy Chung always
    remember the morning of the first match of the season in
    August 1996?

12. Goalkeeper Jim Stannard kept an amazing 29 clean sheets
    during the 1995–6 season, a club record – but with which
    club?

13. Nicknamed 'Budgie' he was capped by England when in
    the Third Division in 1962 with Crystal Palace –who is
    he?

14. Who in the 1997–8 season managed Fulham, Swansea and
    Brentford?

15. One time club captain Steve Spriggs held the club record
    of 416 games in the League for which club 1975–87?

NORWICH CITY

1. Which high-profile TV cook is a director of the Norfolk club?

2. Which former Norwich favourite captained Man Utd to the Premiership title?

3. Who scored 25 league goals for the club in 1993–94 before moving to Blackburn Rovers?

4. Which former Ipswich Town player took over as manager of the club in April 2000?

5. Which Second Division club defeated Norwich in the FA Cup semi-final in 1992?

6. Which Welsh striker was the club's leading scorer 1998–1999 and 1999–2000?

7. Who managed the Carrow Road club from 1992 to 1994 before taking over the reigns at Everton?

8. Which side eventually ended Norwich's hopes in the UEFA Cup in the 1993–94?

9. Who set a record in the Premiership by scoring four times against Everton in September 1993?

10. Who joined Arsenal for £1.2million in 1990 and then went on to score an FA Cup-winning goal?

11. In 1992–3 Norwich finished third in the Premiership - which former Old Trafford player top-scored with 15 league goals?

12. Which non-league club did Norwich defeat 8–0 in a FA Cup tie in 1989?

13. Which Division Four side did Norwich defeat in the League Cup final in 1962?

14. Which full-back won 35 of his 41 caps for Wales whilst with Norwich after leaving Spurs?

15. Norwich reached their second League Cup final in 1973, losing 1–0 to which side?

IPSWICH TOWN

1. Who left Ipswich for Newcastle in July 1999 for £6 million and then won England caps?

2. Once with Manchester United, this striker scored 22 league goals for Ipswich Town in 1999–2000, who is he?

3. Which Ipswich player made his England debut against Malta in June 2000?

4. Which goalkeeper conceded nine goals to Man Utd in a Premiership game in March 1995?

5. Who managed the club when it won the Third, Second and First Division Championships in the 1950s and 1960s?

6. Which player did they purchase for a club record fee of £2.5 million from Huddersfield in February 2000?

7. Later to join Spurs in 1984 he became the youngest scorer in the top flight of English football at the age of 16 years 57 days?

8. Who is the only Ipswich player to score in an FA Cup final?

9. Which Scottish international once scored five times in a Division One game against Southampton in 1982?

10. Who was the Ipswich striker who scored twice on his England debut against Wales in 1975?

11. Who scored against Ipswich in the 1981 UEFA Cup final and played in the Football League for Forest and Spurs?

12. Which Ipswich player in 1981 became the first overseas international to win the Football Writers' Association Player of the Year?

13. Which former FA Cup-winning manager was in charge of the club between 1990 and 1994?

14. Against which club did Ipswich suffer their biggest defeat, 10–1, on Boxing Day 1963, the last time a side conceded 10 goals in a top-flight game in England?

15. Which player scored a record 203 league goals for the club in two spells: 1958–1963 and 1966–1969?

FA CUP – General

1. Which side during the 1990s played in two FA Cup finals and won them both?

2. Which non-league side took Charlton Athletic to a replay in the FA Cup Third round in 2000–1?

3. Who was manager of Manchester United when they won the FA Cup twice in the 1980s?

4. Who scored both of Chelsea's goals in their 2–1 FA Cup semi-final win against Newcastle at Wembley in 2000?

5. Which was the last club to have won the FA Cup wearing red and white-striped shirts?

6. Who managed different clubs in Wembley FA Cup finals in 1982 and 1991?

7. Whose memorable goal of the season drew Hereford level in their shock defeat of Newcastle in the FA Cup in 1972?

8. Which current Premiership manager was the only man to appear in FA Cup Finals in the 1970s, 1980s and 90s?

9. Which club were beaten in two semi-finals by Manchester United in the 1990s?

10. Apart from West Brom which other club won the FA Cup in both the 1950s and 1960s?

11. Which Spurs player is credited with scoring at both ends in the Coventry-Spurs 1987 final?

12. Who were the brothers who appeared in Manchester United's 1977 Cup final victory over Liverpool?

13. Who made history in 1989 and 1995 by becoming the first player to win FA Cup winner's medals with both Liverpool and Everton?

14. The winning goal scorers in the 1970, 1973 and 1982 FA Cup finals went onto manage which club in the 1990s?

15. Which side in an FA Cup final in the 1990s featured a father and son as manager and player respectively?

THE PLAY-OFFS

1. Which side won promotion to the Premiership in 2000 by winning the First Division play-off final?
2. Who was the manager of Blackburn Rovers when they won promotion to the new Premier League after beating Leicester City in the 1992 play-off final?
3. Which side famously drew 4–4 in the First Division play-off final with Charlton in 1998 before losing on penalties?
4. And in that game which Charlton player scored the first ever hat-trick in a play-off final at Wembley?
5. Which side won the Second Division play-off final in 1999 on penalties, after scoring two late goals to draw 2–2 with Gillingham?
6. Which side was promoted to the First Division in 1990 despite losing in the Second Division play-off final?
7. Which future successful Premiership manager was in charge of Wycombe Wanderers when they won the 1994 Third Division final at Wembley?
8. Which side came from two goals down to beat Reading 4–3 in the 1995 First Division final?
9. Later to score the winning goal in a League Cup final, who scored Leicester City's winner in the last minute of extra time to beat Crystal Palace in the 1996 First Division final?
10. Which TV pundit was in charge of Bradford City when they beat Notts County in the 1996 Second Division final?
11. Which current Premiership boss was in charge of Swindon when they defeated Leicester City 4–3 in the 1993 First Division final to reach the Premiership?
12. When the play-offs were revived in 1987 which side remained in the old First Division by defeating Leeds United in a two-legged final?
13. Still with the club, he scored both Leicester City's goals when they beat Derby County 2–1 in the 1994 First Division final. Who is he?
14. Now playing in Division Two, in 1991 they become the only side to reach the English top flight by winning play-off finals in two consecutive seasons. Who are they?
15. In 1988 which side dropped out of the top flight when losing to promoted Middlesbrough 2–1 on aggregate in the play-offs?

BRITISH CLUBS IN EUROPE

1.　Which player scored European hat-tricks for both Newcastle United and Manchester United in the 1990s?

2.　Which international goalkeeper is the only Englishman to play over 100 matches in European competitions – doing so from 1969–84?

3.　Who scored in all eight of Arsenal's matches in the 1994–95 Cup Winners Cup prior to the final?

4.　Later to manage the club, who captained Celtic to victory in the 1967 European Cup final against Inter Milan?

5.　Which side inflicted Manchester United's biggest defeat in a Champions Cup game: 4–0 in 1994?

6.　Which famous England international's only goals for an English club in Europe were when scoring twice for Spurs against Porto in the 1991–92 Cup Winners Cup?

7.　Who is the only Arsenal player to score four times in a European match, doing so against FK Austria in the 1991 European Champions Cup?

8.　Which side played their only season in Europe since 1963 when appearing in the UEFA Cup in 1992–93, going out in the second round?

9.　In 1970–71 which forward scored five goals in the Cup Winners Cup for Cardiff before scoring once for Liverpool in the Fairs Cup later in the season?

10.　Which Welsh side have recorded their biggest ever victory in the Cup Winners Cup, 12–0 against Sliema Wanderers of Malta in 1982?

11.　Which English ground was used as a neutral venue when Celtic played Rapid Vienna in the Cup Winners Cup in 1984, after crowd trouble at Parkhead caused the second leg to be replayed?

12.　When Ipswich Town played in the European Cup in 1961–62 which centre-forward scored five times in a game against Floriana of Malta?

13.　Which side, later to reach the final, knocked Aston Villa out of the European Cup in 1982–83 when the English side defended the trophy?

14.　Which centre-forward twice scored four times in a match for Ipswich Town in the UEFA Cup, against Lazio in 1973 and Landskrona of Sweden in 1977?

15.　Chelsea won the 1971 Cup Winners Cup final, but which other English side (the holders) did they beat in the semi?

THE EUROPEAN CUP

1. Who was the Scottish international who scored the only goal of the game when Nottingham Forest won the trophy for a second time in 1980?

2. Which side did Manchester United beat to win the trophy for the first time in 1968?

3. He would later become a TV personality and in 1977 captained Liverpool to the trophy for the first time?

4. Who scored Ajax's only goal of the 1996 final and would join Liverpool in 2001?

5. Between 1988–92 only four players scored in the final – and they all played international football for which country?

6. David Stewart kept goal for which English side in the European Cup final?

7. Which German side won the competition on three successive occasions in the 1970s?

8. Who was the legendary Celtic manager when they won the trophy in 1967?

9. In 1992 which side won the trophy for the first time in their history by beating Sampdoria 1–0?

10. Which Bulgarian side knocked out Nottingham Forest in 1980–81 and Liverpool in 1981–82 when they were both holders of the trophy?

11. Which Italian side reached the final for the only time in 1957?

12. The only pair of brothers to appear for an English side in the final, did so for Leeds in 1975, who are they?

13. Which European Cup winning side were nicknamed the 'Lisbon Lions'?

14. Which Dutch international scored the late winner for Ajax in the 1995 final after coming on as a substitute?

15. Which club ended Real Madrid's quest for a sixth consecutive European Cup in 1960–61, before losing 3–2 to Benfica in the Final?

ENGLAND

1. Who took over as England captain after the 1990 World Cup finals?

2. Which African country have England twice played in internationals at Wembley, winning both games 2–0 in February 1991 and November 1997?

3. Who was Graham Taylor's assistant when he was the manager of England between 1990 and 1993?

4. Who have been England's only opponents in a World Cup third-place play-off game?

5. In May 1980 which of the home countries was the last side to score four times against England, when winning 4–1?

6. Which Spurs player scored on his England debut at Wembley in November 1979?

7. Which forward scored his first goal for England in the 2–1 win over Malta in June 2000?

8. Which Manchester City forward won his only England cap against Spain in September 1992?

9. Which Premiership ground staged England's first home game outside Wembley for 29 years in 1995 in a 3–3 draw against Sweden?

10. Whose mistake led to the Polish goal in the 1–1 draw at Wembley in October 1973 when they qualified for the World Cup finals at England's expense?

11. Which player during the 1980s scored in the first minute of internationals for England on three occasions, including goals after 38 and 44 seconds of matches at Wembley?

12. England qualified for the 1982 World Cup finals in Spain after defeating which country 1–0 at Wembley?

13. Geoff Hurst scored two hat-tricks for England, one is well known but against which other World Cup winning country did he score the other, in a 5–0 win at Wembley in March 1969?

14. Which great player won 18 England caps in his career from April 1955 to November 1957?

15. Which defender was England's most capped player of the 1970s, winning 57 of his 62 caps during the decade?

SCOTLAND

1. Who succeeded Andy Roxburgh as Scotland boss in 1993?

2. Who is the only player to have won over 100 caps for Scotland?

3. Which current player has scored the winning goal for Scotland in away games against England and Germany?

4. Which goalkeeper made his Scotland debut against Wales in May 1997?

5. Now a TV personality he scored his first goals for Scotland against Hungary in September 1987?

6. Which famous player is the youngest Scottish international when being capped in 1958 aged just 18 yrs 235 days?

7. Which Everton player in the Premiership in 2000–1 season scored Scotland's winning goal against England at Hampden Park in 1985?

8. In the 1998 World Cup who became the first Scottish player sent-off in the final stages, doing so against Morocco?

9. Which player in the 1990s was capped for Scotland whilst with Motherwell, Borussia Dortmund and Celtic?

10. Which country did Scotland play in the World Cup final stages of 1974, 1982 and 1990 and 1998?

11. Which country did Scotland beat 2–0 in a play-off to qualify for the 1986 World Cup finals?

12. Who was the Scotland manager when they qualified for the World Cup Finals in 1974?

13. Which Scottish forward was capped for his country in the 1980s whilst playing for AC Milan?

14. Against which country did Scotland record their only victory in the 1992 European Championships: 3–0 in their final match?

15. Who were the brothers capped for Scotland in the 1970s, one with Liverpool and the other with Partick Thistle?

QUICKFIRE

1. Which legendary goalscorer died at Goodison Park in 1980 after watching the Merseyside derby?

2. Which striker did Leeds United sign from Sunderland for £5million in 1999?

3. Who during Euro 2000 was distinguishable for the 'shades' he wore during his team matches?

4. Which club won the last ever Football League First Division title prior to the formation of the Premiership?

5. Who scored his only two goals in over 50 England internationals in the 7–1 win over San Marino in 1993?

6. Which club's nickname is the 'Shaymen', taken from their ground – The Shay?

7. Who used to play at Leeds Road and were the first club to win the Championship in three successive seasons?

8. Which player appeared in the 1980 and 1987 FA Cup Final with West Ham and Tottenham respectively?

9. Which Frenchman scored two hat-tricks in the 1984 European Championships?

10. Which legendary player won 88 caps in total – 84 for Hungary and four for Spain?

11. When Coventry were in the Third Division in the 1950s their goalkeeper achieved the rare distinction of winning an England cap –who was he?

12. Which club lost on their own ground in the European Cup final to an English club?

13. In 1984 Didier Six was the first French player to appear in the English top flight, with which club?

14. Which man made over 300 appearances for two league clubs, Spurs and Fulham?

15. For which side did Andy Gray appear in the 1974 Scottish FA Cup final with Everton manager Walter Smith?

QUICKFIRE

1. Which Division One side in the 2000–1 season play at Blundell Park in Cleethorpes?

2. Which club remained in the Premiership on the final day of the 1999–2000 season when beating Liverpool 1–0?

3. Which TV pundit captained Liverpool to the League and Cup double in 1986?

4. Which man left Bradford to manage Sheffield Wednesday in 2000?

5. Later to manage two Championship-winning sides, he played in losing FA Cup finals for Preston and Everton in the 1960s – who is he?

6. Which Italian goalkeeper did Alex Ferguson sign during the 1999–2000 season?

7. Graeme Souness has managed two clubs in the Premiership up to the end of the 2000–1 season, Liverpool and which other club?

8. Which was the first club to appear in the finals of all three European competitions?

9. Which goalkeeper was ever-present in the Leicester City side from 1975 to 1981?

10. Who was the player who scored a record 42 goals for Leeds United in the 1953–4 season and was also a world class centre-half?

11. Which man is the only player to win FA Cup winner's medals with both North London clubs?

12. Who played in the 1988 and 1990 FA Cup finals for Wimbledon and Crystal Palace respectively?

13. Which goalkeeper conceded nine goals in a game at Anfield in 1989?

14. Which former West Brom player was sent-off a record 21 times in his career and was also sent home in disgrace from Scotland's World Cup squad in 1978?

15. In 1966, which was the last club to win the League Cup final over two legs?

The Group phase

1. Which four clubs in the Football league in 2000–1 begin with the letter 'H'?
   (4 points)

2. Which three men have managed clubs to victory in the League Cup final on three or more occasions?
   (3 points)

3. With which five clubs did centre-half Dave Watson play for England between 1974 and 1982?
   (5 points)

Penalty Shoot-out

1. Which Division One side plays at Oakwell?

2. With which club was Ian Wright last capped for England?

3. Who was the first Englishman to score for a foreign side in a European Cup final?

4. Who bowed out of international football in 2000 after making 150 international appearances for Germany?

5. For which country does Coventry player Mustapha Hadji play international football?

Full-time

In 1998 Brian Deane finished his Sheffield United career away to Sunderland, at the Stadium of Light. He then moved to Benfica, who of course play at the other Stadium of Light.

'From the Stadium of Light to the edge of darkness' – Birmingham City fan after Jose Dominguez of Benfica arrived for a 21–day trial.

During Bolton's home game against Everton in the 1997–98 season cameras clearly showed the ball crossing the Everton goal-line during a goalmouth scramble, the end result being a 0–0 draw instead of a 1–0 home win. At the end of the season Bolton were relegated on goal difference . . . from Everton.

The Group phase

1.   Chelsea appeared in three FA Cup finals at Wembley from
     1994 to 2000 – which three goalkeepers played for them?
     (3 points)

2.   At the start of the 2000–1 season which six players had
     scored 100 or more goals in the Premiership?
     (6 points)

3.   In June 1991, against New Zealand, Crystal Palace
     provided three players in an England side for the first time
     – who were they?
     (3 points)

Penalty Shoot-out

1.   Of which chairman did Derby County fans chant: 'He's
     fat, he's round, he's never at the ground'?

2.   In August 1999 which Newcastle player was sent-off for
     the first time in an illustrious career against Aston Villa?

3.   Who was the Argentinean striker Derby County signed in
     September 1999, only later to be refused re-entry to
     Britain over a passport irregularity?

4.   In the 2000 League Cup final who became the first
     woman to officiate in a major Wembley final?

5.   Who were the amateur side who lost to Nantes in the 2000
     French Cup final?

Full-time

Although Ian Rush scored five goals in FA Cup finals, he was not the first 'rush' to appear on the final score-sheet. A goal scored by the Royal Engineers in the 1878 final is credited as a 'rush' as the scorer is not known from a group of players who claimed the goal.

Cricket commentator Chris Cowdrey at the Sri Lanka-England test match in 2001 on hearing the European Cup draw: 'That's great news – we've got three clubs left and they've all got home draws.' Geoff Boycott: 'Stick to cricket, Chris, they're the first legs.'

The classic 'phantom goal' was the one scored by Alan Hudson of Chelsea against Ipswich Town on 26 September 1970, whose shot hit the stanchion on the outside of the goal and bounced back onto the pitch. The referee, believing the ball to have rebounded from the stanchion inside the net, awarded a goal. Chelsea won 2–1.

BRITISH CLUBS

1. Which is the only club to win the League Cup on penalties?

2. Apart from Manchester United, which is the only other club to do 'the Double' in England more than once?

3. Who in January 1999 became the costliest Welshman when moving from West Ham to Wimbledon?

4. Which North East club has had to apply for re-election on a 11 occasions?

5. Who was the manager of Manchester United prior to Sir Alex Ferguson?

6. Of which club are the Gallagher brothers of Oasis followers?

7. At which ground did Ryan Giggs score his 'wonder-goal' for Manchester United against Arsenal in a 1999 FA Cup semi-final?

8. Who scored a rare hat-trick of headers for Bolton in a FA Cup match in 2000–1?

9. Kevin Keegan, Ray Clemence and Ian Botham all played home league games at the Old Show Ground – which club once played there?

10. Who is the former Wales international who has been in charge of Wrexham since 1989?

11. Which Yorkshire club returned to the League in 1998 after winning the Conference – five years after losing league status?

12. What was unusual about Sam Wynne's four goals scored against Manchester United for Oldham in 1923?

13. Which then Third Division side, in their best FA Cup performance, were beaten by Watford in a 1984 semi-final?

14. For which club did father and son Ian and Gary Bowyer play together in 1990?

15. Stoke City's winning goal in the 1972 League Cup final was scored by a player who ten years earlier had been a key figure in the lifting of the maximum wage – who was he?

BRITISH CLUBS

1. Who was sacked as Spurs manager in March 2001?

2. Appropriately on St Patrick's Day 2001, who was captain
    for the day on his 500th first team appearance for
    Manchester United?

3. Which current Premiership manager appeared for Rangers
    in the 1969 Scottish Cup final?

4. Which club lost just three league games in the 1998–99
    season but could only finish third in the Premiership
    behind Manchester United and Arsenal?

5. When Gerard Houllier came to Liverpool in 1998 he was
    originally joint manager with which man?

6. Which goalkeeper became Bradford City's oldest ever
    player in the 1999–2000 season at 41 years 178 days after
    also winning 92 caps?

7. In 1974 which was the first side to win the Charity Shield
    on penalties?

8. What is the surname of the father who played for
    Sheffield Wednesday in the 1966 FA Cup final, and his
    son who was manager of West Brom in the 2000–1
    season?

9. Which club did Sam Allardyce leave to become Bolton
    manager in October 1999?

10. On Boxing Day 1999, which became the first Football
    League club to field a side with no English players in a
    match at Southampton?

11. Which member of the Spurs double-winning side of 1961
    would later manage a title-winning side in England?

12. Who was voted Scottish Manager of the Year in 1999 and
    2000?

13. Which man was voted the Manager of the Year in England
    whilst with Aston Villa on two occasions?

14. Which club is nicknamed 'the Choirboys'?

15. When Middlesbrough played Preston in 1973 who were
    the brothers who managed the two sides?

COVENTRY CITY

1. For which player did Coventry City receive a fee of £13 million in 2000?

2. Now with Manchester City, in 1998–99 he scored hat-tricks on consecutive weekends against Nottingham Forest in the league and Macclesfield in the FA Cup?

3. Which Coventry goalkeeper played in both Sweden's internationals against England in the qualifying rounds of Euro 2000?

4. Which Coventry City player was joint leading scorer in the Premiership in 1997–98?

5. Which Coventry player retired at the end of the 1999–2000 season having played top flight football in each of the last four decades?

6. Who did Gordon Strachan replace as manager of the club in November 1996?

7. Which TV pundit and presenter was manager of Coventry when they entered the First Division in 1967 for the first time?

8. Which Australian international did Gordon Strachan sign from Portsmouth in the 1998–99 season?

9. Coventry had only one representative in the 1998 World Cup, but he scored for Romania against England – who is he?

10. Which centre-half left the club in 1994 for £3.6 million after starring for the Republic of Ireland in the 1994 World Cup?

11. In 1996 Aberdeen received a record fee of £1.75 million for which player from Coventry?

12. Which overseas player for Coventry scored the first hat-trick by an opposition player against Liverpool at Anfield for 33 years in 1995?

13. Which bulky centre forward scored a hat-trick against Arsenal on the opening day of the 1993–94 season?

14. Which England international defender managed the club between 1990 and 1992?

15. Which future international manager had the first of his two spells in charge of the club in 1983–84?

LEICESTER CITY

1. Which veteran striker top scored for Leicester City in league matches in the 1999–2000 season with 13 goals?

2. Which Leicester City defender captained Northern Ireland on his 50th international appearance in February 2001?

3. Who was Leicester City's only representative in England's 1966 World Cup-winning side?

4. Who made his Leicester City debut in 1966 aged 16 and was still playing league football 30 years later?

5. Which Leicester player made his England debut against Belgium in October 1999?

6. From which club did they sign Robbie Savage?

7. Which club beat Leicester in the 1969 FA Cup when the Foxes last appeared in the final?

8. Who was the Millwall manager in the 2000–1 season who had been in charge of Leicester in the 1994–95 season?

9. Who was Leicester City's unused goalkeeper in the 2000 League Cup final who was Liverpool's unused 'keeper in the final twelve months later?

10. When Leicester City's youngest ever player, Dave Buchanan, made his debut for the club on 1 January 1979, which future international player also made his league debut?

11. Later to become the most expensive player in English football, in 1969 for Leicester, he became the youngest captain of a FA Cup final side when aged 21 years 212 days. Who is he?

12. Who scored a hat-trick on his home debut against Sunderland in March 2000?

13. Which Spanish side knocked Leicester out of the Cup Winners' Cup in 1961–62 and when they next appeared in Europe in the UEFA Cup 36 years later?

14. Who played in Leicestershire's County Cricket Championship win in 1975 having played in two of Leicester's FA Cup finals of the 1960s?

15. Who won 39 caps for Northern Ireland at centre-half from 1980 to 1987 whilst with Leicester to become the club's most capped player?

THE SCOTTISH CUPS

1. Which side memorably knocked Celtic out of the Scottish Cup in 1999–2000, with a 3–1 win at Celtic Park in the third round?

2. Which current Premiership boss managed the Scottish Cup winners three times during the 1990s?

3. Which England international goalkeeper went a British record of over 13 hours without conceding a goal until beaten by Hamilton's Adrian Sprott in a shock 1–0 defeat for Rangers in the Scottish Cup in 1987?

4. Which side won the Scottish FA Cup four times in the 1980s?

5. Teams from which city contested the Scottish League Cup final in November 1980?

6. Which pair of brothers played in FA Cup finals both north and south of the border in the 1990s – one for Manchester United and the other for Rangers?

7. Who was the former Aston Villa player who scored for Rangers in both Scottish League Cup finals of 1989 and 1990?

8. Which club beat Falkirk 1–0 in 1997 to win the Scottish Cup for the first time since 1929?

9. Which international was the only Englishman to win FA Cup winners medals both north and south of the border during the 1990s?

10. Which club lost in seven out of eight Scottish League Cup finals from 1971 to 1978?

11. He won the Scottish Cup three times with Aberdeen in the 1980s and then played for Manchester United when they won the FA Cup in 1985 – who is he?

12. Which club's last trophy in Scotland was when they beat Dundee 2–0 in the Scottish League Cup final in November 1995?

13. Who was the former Chelsea and Spurs striker who scored a hat-trick for Rangers in their 5–1 Scottish Cup Final win over Hearts in 1996?

14. What was unique about Aberdeen's victory over Celtic in the 1990 Scottish Cup final?

15. Which current First Division side was the only club to play both Rangers (in 1992) and Celtic (1995) in Scottish FA Cup finals during the decade?

FA CUP – THE 1990s

1.   Who during the decade became the first sponsors of the trophy?

2.   In 1997 who became the first foreigner to manage an FA Cup-winning side?

3.   Which side appeared in an FA Cup final for the first time in 24 years in 1998?

4.   Which famous manager made his only appearance as a boss in the final in 1991?

5.   Who during the decade scored the fastest goal in an FA Cup final at Wembley?

6.   In the 1993 Arsenal-Tottenham semi-final at Wembley who scored the only goal of the game?

7.   Which then Second Division club were beaten on penalties by Liverpool in an FA Cup semi-final replay at Villa Park in 1992?

8.   In their classic semi-final at Villa Park in 1999 which Arsenal player had a last-minute penalty saved by Peter Schmiechel?

9.   Tim Buzaglo was a hat-trick hero for which non-league side in 1991?

10. Which player appeared for Manchester United in the final in 1990 and Middlesbrough in 1997?

11. Which side eventually ended Tranmere's giant-killing run in the 2000–1 season in the FA Cup?

12. Which Premiership side last reached the FA Cup semi-final when losing 4–1 to Nottingham Forest in 1991?

13. Which player was sent-off in FA Cup semi-finals at Villa Park in 1995 and 1999, the first player to have been ordered off twice at that stage?

14. Against which side in the 1998–99 FA Cup were Arsenal ordered to replay their tie after a controversial winning goal at Highbury?

15. Which Premiership side lost their only semi-final of the decade 3–0 to Liverpool at Old Trafford in 1996?

EUROPEAN CLUBS

1.   Which side has won the Dutch league title on a record number of occasions?

2.   Inter Bratislava in 2000 won which country's league title?

3.   Who captained Bayern Munich to three consecutive European Cup triumphs in the 1970s?

4.   He managed Everton to two league titles and managed Athletic Bilbao between 1987 and 1989?

5.   Which German player was the European Footballer of the Year in 1980 and 1981?

6.   Spartak, Dinamo, CSKA, Torpedo and Lokomotiv are all club sides based in which city?

7.   Which striker was sold by Sampdoria to Juventus for a then world record fee of £12.5 million in June 1992?

8.   Later to play for Leeds United he was the leading scorer in the Bundesliga whilst with Eintracht Frankfurt in 1992–93?

9.   Which club won eight Portuguese titles in the 1990s?

10.   For which other Italian side did Ruud Gullit play apart from AC Milan?

11.   Which club were French champions in 2000 but were eliminated with Rangers in Group D of the Champions League in 2000–1?

12.   Still playing in the Premiership he was one of the most expensive players in history when moving from Lazio to Juventus for £3.5 million in May 1990 – who is he?

13.   Which club won the Dutch title for the only time in 1981, the same year when they lost to Ipswich in the UEFA Cup final?

14.   Which French club sold David Ginola to Newcastle United in 1995?

15.   Who is the most expensive player ever to come from Eastern Europe, costing AC Milan £15.7 million in 1999?

EUROPEAN CHAMPIONS CUP

1.   Who top-scored for Chelsea with eight goals in their 1999–2000 European Cup campaign?

2.   Who was the famous Brazilian international who won a winner's medal with Real Madrid in 2000?

3.   Later to manage Crystal Palace, he played for Sampdoria in the 1992 European Cup final at Wembley – who is he?

4.   Which Juventus player was the highest scorer in the European Cup in the 1997–98 season with 10 goals, including a semi-final hat-trick against Monaco?

5.   Who scored twice for Real Madrid when they beat Manchester United 3–2 in the 2000–1 European Cup quarter-finals?

6.   When Monaco knocked Manchester United out of the European Cup in 1997–98 who was the Scotland captain in their side?

7.   When Manchester United won the European Cup in 1999 who was their leading scorer in the competition with eight goals?

8.   Which current Premiership player won European Cup medals with Marseille in 1993 and AC Milan in 1994?

9.   Englishman Bobby Houghton managed which club against an English side in the European Cup final?

10. In which city did Liverpool beat Real Madrid 1–0 in the 1981 European Cup final?

11. Which side lost their first of six finals in the competition 4–1 to AC Milan in 1969?

12. Who were the brothers who appeared for Ajax in the 1996 European Cup final against Juventus?

13. Which defender was the only Liverpool player to appear in their five European Cup finals from 1977–85?

14. Which side, managed by Sven Goran-Eriksson, knocked Arsenal out of the 1991–92 European Cup 4–2 on aggregate?

15. Which fellow Blackburn Rovers player was involved in a fracas on the pitch with David Batty in a Champions Cup match in 1995?

WORLD CUP - General

1.   Which country won the World Cup for the first time in 1958?

2.   Which country did the USA face in an emotionally charged game in the 1998 finals in the group stages – a game they lost 2–1?

3.   Who was the last player to score in a World Cup Final whilst playing his club football in England?

4.   Whose penalty settled the 1990 West Germany-Argentina Final?

5.   Which country shocked the European giants Italy by 1–0 in a group match at Ayresome Park in 1966?

6.   Which country won the first ever tournament in 1930 by defeating Argentina in the Final?

7.   Who created history by managing Brazil to victory in the 1970 Final having won a World Cup winner's medal as a player in 1962?

8.   The greatest team of their time, they scored 27 goals in the 1954 tournament only to lose in the final – who were they?

9.   Which is the only African country to reach the World Cup quarter-finals?

10. Which Italian top scored in the 1982 tournament with six goals?

11. Who was the 'cat-like' goalkeeper for Brazil in the 1970 World Cup Final?

12. Which European country has reached the final on two occasions – the last when losing 3–1 to Brazil in 1962?

13. Two future managers of Germany played in the 1974 final, Franz Beckenbauer and who else?

14. Wembley staged one of the semi-finals in 1966, but which ground staged the other?

15. In which year did the only World Cup Final take place which featured the host country against the reigning holders?

ENGLAND – General

1. Which England manager in 1962 lost his first game in charge by 5–2 to France in a qualifying game for the European Championships?

2. Who against Czechoslovakia in May 1963 became England's youngest ever captain at 22 years 47 days?

3. Who was England's leading scorer of the 1990s with 27 goals in the decade?

4. Which Manchester United player's appearance against the Republic of Ireland in 1991 was the first by a teenager for England for eight years?

5. Which West Ham centre-half played his only game for England in the final stages of the World Cup against Paraguay in 1986?

6. Against which African country did Michael Owen score his first England goal in May 1998?

7. Which defender scored only his second England goal in June 2000 against Malta eight years after the first for his country?

8. Prior to the Nevilles, who had been the last pair of brothers capped by England?

9. In the qualifying games for Euro 2000, who scored a hat-trick for England and in another game was sent-off?

10. Which defender has won over 30 caps for England, with just one goal scored against Luxembourg in 1998?

11. Who was the last player capped for England whilst with Sheffield United, winning three caps in 1991 and 1992?

12. Which England manager won the most caps for his country as a player?

13. In 1995 who became the second Wimbledon player capped by England?

14. In 1977 against Argentina who became the third Englishman sent off in a full international?

15. Which forward in the late 1970s was capped by England whilst with a German club?

QUICKFIRE

1. Which England international won the League Cup with both Leicester City and Stoke City?

2. In the England against Scotland game in Euro 96, who scored for England past his club goalkeeper?

3. Which player did Arsenal sign from Juventus for a fee of £10 million in August 1999?

4. Which country beat England at Wembley 6–3 in November 1953 and 7–1 in May 1954?

5. Which Leeds United player in March 2001 scored the club's fastest ever goal in the Premiership goal after just 11 seconds against Charlton?

6. Which London club was not allowed to compete in the first European Cup in 1955–56 following their only title win?

7. Mario Basler has scored a goal for which club in a European Cup final against an English side?

8. Which goalkeeper won his first England cap in 1989 after 340 league appearances?

9. Which West Brom forward in 1965–66 is the only player to have scored in every round of the League Cup in the same season, including the final?

10. Which was the first club to win a FA Cup final replay at Wembley?

11. Which former West Ham player resigned as manager of Barnet in March 2001?

12. Apart from England which other country was involved in two penalty shoot-outs at Euro '96?

13. From which Spanish side did John Aldridge join Tranmere Rovers in 1991?

14. Which legendary Newcastle player succeeded Sir Alf Ramsey as Ipswich manager in 1963?

15. Who were the brothers who faced each other when they managed York City and Stoke City in a league game in November 1998?

QUICKFIRE

1. For which Italian club did Robbie Keane play?

2. In 2001 who was the first player to score a goal in a major final held at the Millennium Stadium?

3. Who was better known as 'The Wizard of Dribble' who died in February 2000?

4. Who were the brothers, Graham and Ray, who played for Chelsea in the 1970s?

5. Which club play at the Vetch Field?

6. Which current Leeds defender has won England under-21 caps but has played for Scotland in a full international?

7. Which Eastern European country were runners-up in the Olympic soccer finals in 1948, 1952 and 1956?

8. Which African country first played in the World Cup finals in 1970?

9. By what name was the Scottish club side Livingston formerly known?

10. Who was the first Channel Islander to start an England international?

11. What is the Christian name of the Neville brothers' father?

12. Which player scored 30 goals for Scotland between 1971 and 1986?

13. In 1985, which became the first side to win all three major European trophies?

14. Goalkeeper Thomas Ravelli has won over 100 caps for which country?

15. In which country did Arsene Wenger manager before joining Arsenal?

The Group phase

1. Which two clubs won the FA Cup in the 1960s, 1970s and 1980s?
    (2 points)

2. Which eight international players have scored for four (or more) different clubs in the Premiership at March 2001 – three English, three Welsh, one Scot and one Romanian?
    (8 points)

3. Which two Division One managers in the 2000–1 season have won European Cup winner's medals?
    (2 points)

Penalty Shoot-out

1. Who scored a hat-trick against Wales for Holland in a World Cup qualifier in 1996?

2. Which World Cup winner joined Arsenal for a British record transfer fee of £220,000 in December 1971?

3. Against which country did Glenn Hoddle score on his England debut in 1979?

4. Which current Fulham player equalled the Conference record fee of £250,000 when he moved from Stevenage Borough to Bristol Rovers in August 1997?

5. Why were both Derek Hales and Mike Flanagan of Charlton Athletic sent off in a FA Cup tie in 1979?

Full-time

Gordon Strachan is the only man to have been voted Player of the Year both north and south of the border, winning the Writers' award in 1980 with Aberdeen and Leeds United in 1991.

'All these rumours about my private life are unfounded – both my wives are upset about them' – Malcolm Allison

Several players have been transferred to and from clubs for large sums, without playing a single game. Clive Allen went to Arsenal from QPR in the summer of 1980, only to move to Crystal Palace before the start of the season in exchange for Kenny Sansom. David Unsworth was at Aston Villa for six days in July 1998 after a £3 million move from West Ham before returning to Everton. Coventry made £750,000 profit on Robert Jarni in 1998; he was with the Highfield Road club for just a couple of days after moving from Real Betis and was then sold to Real Madrid.

The Group phase

1. Which three players – whilst with Newcastle, Leeds United and Aston Villa respectively – have been capped by England in two different spells at the same club?
   (3 points)

2. With two players have twice scored four goals in a game for England in post-war internationals?
   (2 points)

3. Apart from Glen Hoddle, which seven managers in the Premiership at March 2001 had also played for the club they are currently in charge of?
   (7 points)

Penalty Shoot-out

1. Which country was beaten in the World Cup semi-finals in both 1982 and 1986?

2. Who was the former Republic of Ireland striker who managed Bradford City between 1991 and 1994?

3. Who was the Tottenham manager who signed Osvaldo Ardiles in 1978?

4. Who captained England for a record number of occasions in the 1950s?

5. Which goalkeeper for Aston Villa in 1994 saved five penalties in two consecutive matches, three in a penalty shoot-out with Tranmere Rovers and two against Tottenham?

Full-time

On 5 September 1992 John Fashanu scored for Wimbledon in the 81st minute of a game against Arsenal, at the same time his brother Justin was being sent-off for Torquay. In the 1978 World Cup the van de Kerkhof brothers each scored in the 82nd minute of consecutive games for Holland.

'I'm sorry Graham, I'm afraid there's only 20 minutes of the programme left so I'm going to have to take you off' – Gary Lineker to Graham Taylor on *Football Focus*.

In 1976 George Best nearly became the first player to receive a red card in a league match, receiving one whilst with Fulham shortly after the first recipient, David Wagstaffe of Blackburn. In an Italian amateur game between Pianta and Arpax, Fernando D'Ercoli showed his disgust at the referee sending him off by snatching the red card and eating it.

BRITISH CLUBS

1.   What nationality is Leeds United's Mark Viduka?

2.   Who is Manchester United's assistant manager to Sir Alex Ferguson who was also one of England's coaching staff?

3.   Who was the manager of Wimbledon between 1992 and 1999?

4.   Which team do you associate with TV chat show host Michael Parkinson?

5.   Who scored a last minute equaliser for Birmingham City from the penalty spot against Liverpool in the 2001 Worthington Cup final?

6.   Now manager of the club in 1989–90 who scored ten goals for Oldham Athletic on their way to the League Cup final?

7.   Which Premiership manager in the 2000–1 season had managed the UEFA Cup winners 20 years before?

8.   In April 1994 Wolves appointed which former England manager as their boss?

9.   Who scored twice for Everton in the 1966 FA Cup final even though his name did not figure in the official match programme?

10. Which club are nicknamed 'the Gulls' and play at Plainmoor?

11. Which American goalkeeper did Liverpool sign from Columbus Crew?

12. Who was the Middlesbrough player sent off in a 1997 FA Cup semi-final?

13. Which is the only English side to have played FA Cup ties in all four home countries?

14. Which England international was known as 'Captain Marvel'?

15. In the 1998–99 season who was twice voted Manager of the Month in the Premiership but still saw his side relegated?

BRITISH CLUBS

1. Which Liverpool manager left the post in 1994 following a FA Cup defeat by Bristol City?

2. Which Leeds player missed a penalty against Man Utd in March 2001 after being kicked by Fabien Barthez in the controversial incident that led to the penalty decision?

3. David Moyes has been the manager of which Division One side, in the 2000–1 season, since January 1998?

4. Which Everton player in the 2000–1 season was the Scottish PFA Player of the Year with Dundee United in 1986?

5. Which club plays at Ashton Gate?

6. Who was the first foreign player to captain an FA Cup-winning side?

7. Who took over as manager of Bradford City during the 2000–1 season?

8. In the 1992–93 season which club won their first 11 matches in the new Division One?

9. Where did Reading play their home games prior to their move to the Madejski Stadium?

10. Frank Burrows, Bobby Smith, Jimmy Rimmer, Kevin Cullis and Jan Molby all had a spell as manager of which club in 1995–6?

11. Who scored apart from Roberto di Matteo for Chelsea in the 1998 League Cup final and later played for Leicester in the same final?

12. Who is the only Norwegian to take charge of a Premiership side?

13. Dave and Gary were the christian names of which pair of brothers who played for Manchester City (1981) and Sunderland (1992) respectively in FA Cup finals?

14. Which goalkeeper played in the 1971 FA Cup final aged 21 years and in 1987 when aged 37?

15. Because of an injury crisis who was the wine bar owner, and part-time goalkeeper, who played for Watford in their 1987 FA Cup semi-final against Tottenham?

MIDDLESBROUGH

1. Who became manager of Middlesbrough in May 1994?

2. Who was the Italian who in 1997–8 scored ten goals in his first 12 games for the club?

3. Which England international joined Boro in 1999 from Liverpool for £1,000,000?

4. Which Middlesbrough player appeared in a World Cup game against England in France 98 for Colombia?

5. Which player did they sign in 2000 for a reputed pay packet of £63,000 per week?

6. Which then-Boro player scored a hat trick for Germany against Northern Ireland in September 1999?

7. Which overseas player scored a hat-trick on his Boro debut against Liverpool in August 1996?

8. Who left Middlesbrough for a record fee of £2.3 million in 1989 to join Manchester United with whom he played in four FA Cup finals?

9. Prior to the move to the Riverside what was the name of the club's former ground?

10. Who led Manchester City to many triumphs and then took charge of the Boro from 1982–84?

11. Who kept goal for the club from 1955–56 to 1959–60 and was Brian Clough's assistant at Nottingham Forest?

12. Who was the Division Two's leading scorer in three seasons from 1967–8 to 1970–1 whilst with Middlesbrough?

13. Who in the League Cup semi-final against Liverpool in 1998 scored in both legs – including a penalty after two minutes in the second leg?

14. Which future managerial legend scored five goals for Boro against Brighton in 1958?

15. Which celebrated Middlesbrough forward, with 26 England caps (11 goals) from 1947–52, is the club's most capped Englishman?

LEEDS UNITED

1. Only two men have managed Leeds to the League Championship, Howard Wilkinson and who else?

2. Which England under-21 goalkeeper replaced the injured Nigel Martyn during the 2000–1 season?

3. Who succeeded Howard Wilkinson as manager of the club in 1996?

4. Nigel Martyn was once the country's most expensive goalkeeper when he moved to Elland Road from which club?

5. Which much-travelled striker, whose partner is a famous actress, top-scored for the club with 16 goals when they won the title in 1991–92?

6. Who scored four goals against Liverpool in a league game in the 2000–1 season?

7. Which Leeds United player captained Scotland's 1974 World Cup squad?

8. Which player came to the club for £4.5million in November 1995 from Parma – only to be given a free transfer shortly afterwards?

9. Who captained Leeds in the 1965 FA Cup final in the year he was voted Footballer of the Year?

10. Who scored a controversial 'Hand of God' goal against Leeds in the Champions Cup second stage in March 2001?

11. Which player holds the Leeds record of 168 league goals for the club, in his two spells at Elland Road between 1965 and 1986?

12. When Leeds won the league title in both 1969 and 1974, which player was their top scorer in both seasons with 14 league goals?

13. Which Leeds defender was the first PFA Player of the Year in 1974?

14. Who was the only player to appear under the management of Howard Wilkinson for both club and country?

15. Which player moved to Leeds from the French side Nimes in 1992?

FA CUP – THE 1980s

1.   Which was the only club to win successive finals during the decade?

2.   In the 1989 all-Merseyside final who scored twice for Everton after coming on as a substitute?

3.   Which club reached the final for the only time in its history in 1984?

4.   Which player appeared for QPR in the 1982 final and Spurs in the final five years later?

5.   During the decade who became the first Welsh international to score in the final since Noel Kinsey of Birmingham in 1956?

6.   Which club lost FA Cup semi-finals to Everton in 1984 and Liverpool in 1986?

7.   Which year in the decade saw the last 100,000 attendance for the final?

8.   Which non-league side shocked First Division side Birmingham 2–1 in their 1986 third round tie at St Andrews?

9.   Who was John Sillett's managerial partner when Coventry won the trophy for the first time in their history in 1987?

10.   Which side lost their two semi-final appearances during the decade – to Brighton in 1983 and Everton in 1986?

11.   Which side in 1987 failed to turn up for a third round tie at Anfield due to bad weather and eventually knocked the holders out 3–0 in a replay?

12.   Which Division Three side, managed by Harry Redknapp, knocked the holders Manchester United out in the third round in 1984?

13.   Which West Ham player during the decade became the youngest player to appear in the final at Wembley?

14.   In 1985 who became only the fourth non-league side to reach the fifth round, losing to Everton 3–0?

15.   Which year during the decade saw the last all-London final?

FA CUP – General

1. Which club has won the FA Cup on a record ten occasions?

2. Who is the only player to score for Chelsea in two finals?

3. In 1989 who were the last non-league side to knock a top-division side out of the FA Cup?

4. He scored a famous goal against them for Arsenal, but opened the scoring for Liverpool in the 1992 final – who is he?

5. Later to manage England, he won the FA Cup with Spurs in 1967?

6. Who managed Everton to the trophy in 1984 having set a new record in 1964 for being the youngest player to appear in a Wembley FA Cup Final?

7. Who played for Aston Villa in the 2000 final having appeared for Arsenal in the final seven years earlier?

8. Which player scored for West Brom in every round of the 1967–68 competition including the only goal of the final?

9. Against which side did in the third round in 1990 did Manchester United win 1–0 away in a game that allegedly kept Alex Ferguson at Old Trafford?

10. Who opened the scoring for Liverpool after just two minutes of the all-Merseyside final in 1989?

11. Which current Premiership side played in three FA Cup finals in the 1960s and lost them all?

12. Who scored 38 FA Cup goals in a career in the 1960s and 70s whilst with Fulham, Leicester City and Leeds United amongst others?

13. Which Premiership ground last staged an FA Cup semi-final when Wimbledon beat Luton 2–1 in 1988?

14. Which was the first club to win the FA Cup after the war – beating Charlton 4–2 in the final in 1946?

15. Later to manage Scotland in the World Cup, who appeared in the beaten Blackburn Rovers side in the 1960 final?

EUROPEAN CLUBS

1. Vikingur, Fram and Akranes have won which country's league title in the 1990s?

2. Who is currently the most expensive player in world football, costing £37 million?

3. Which Briton was the manager of Real Sociedad for the third time in his career in 2001?

4. Who played in the 1999 English FA Cup final and the 2000 Portuguese Cup final?

5. Which actor gives his name to the stadium used by the Austrian side Sturm Graz?

6. Which club won the German title five times, all during the 1970s, when they also appeared in the European Cup final?

7. Which current Premiership player was the leading scorer in the Dutch League for three seasons from 1990–93?

8. Which club did the League and Cup double in the Ukraine in 2000?

9. For which club did Ronaldo first play club football in Europe after leaving Brazil?

10. Which club has won the Norwegian title every year since 1992?

11. Two Frenchman were voted European Footballer of the Year in the 1990s – Zinedine Zidane and which striker in 1991?

12. Which club last won the Spanish title in 1971 when they were managed by the legendary Alfredo di Stefano?

13. Which striker's move from River Plate to Lazio in 1998 was then the highest fee paid for a player from an Argentinean club?

14. He moved from TSV Nordlingen to Bayern Munich in 1964 and scored a record 365 goals in the Bundesliga – who is he?

15. Which famous player scored a club record 205 league goals for Ajax in his career?

BRITISH CLUBS IN EUROPE

1.   Who was the Arsenal manager when they won the Cup Winners Cup in 1994?
2.   Who scored eight goals in the two legs when Chelsea beat Jeunesse Hautcharage of Luxembourg 21–0 on aggregate in the Cup Winners Cup in 1971–72?
3.   Which much travelled striker scored a hat-trick for Aston Villa in the UEFA Cup against Stromsgodset of Norway in 1998?
4.   Which Premiership side appeared in Europe for the first time in 36 years in 1997–98 only to lose to Atletico Madrid in the UEFA Cup?
5.   Which English side reached the UEFA Cup in 1999–2000 by winning the Inter-Toto Cup?
6.   Name either of the Arsenal players who missed a penalty in the shoot-out in the 2000 UEFA Cup final?
7.   Which Scottish international scored a record 30 goals in Europe for Leeds from 1965–75?
8.   Which English club's only season in Europe was in the UEFA Cup in 1993–94 when they recorded a memorable aggregate win over Bayern Munich?
9.   Which Scottish Premier League sides best performance in Europe was when they were beaten 4–2 on aggregate by Leeds in the 1966–67 Fairs Cup semi-finals?
10. Which World Cup winner won the Cup Winners Cup with West Ham in 1965 and the UEFA Cup with Spurs in 1972?
11. In which city did Spurs (1963), Aston Villa (1982) and Everton (1985) all win European trophies?
12. Who played for Leeds in the European Champions Cup in 1992–93 and Manchester United in the same competition the following season?
13. Who appeared for Parma when they lost to Arsenal in the 1994 Cup Winners Cup final but won the trophy with Chelsea four years later?
14. Which Scottish club in 1955–56 was the first British side to appear in the European Cup?
15. Which English side was the only club, from any country, to appear in the final of the three major European competitions in the 1970s?

EUROPEAN INTERNATIONALS

1. Who captained France to victory in the 1998 World Cup Final?

2. Which player is Germany's most capped international?

3. Who has scored most international goals in a career for Holland?

4. Which European country finished in third place in the World Cup in both 1974 and 1982?

5. Whose first goal in 120 internationals came for Denmark against Belgium in June 2000?

6. In 2000 who overtook Dino Zoff as Italy's most capped international player?

7. Which famous Hungarian scored a European record of 83 international goals in a career?

8. Which European country reached the semi-final on their first ever appearance in the World Cup finals in 1966?

9. Which former international took charge of Germany when they beat England 1–0 at Wembley in October 2000?

10. Which European is the only man to both captain and manage a World Cup winning side?

11. Which European country shocked Brazil by beating them 2–1 in a Group game at the 1998 World Cup?

12. Which country won the European Championships in their home country in 1968?

13. Who is France's leading scorer in internationals, with 41 goals in 72 games?

14. Which country won all of their ten games in qualifying for the 2000 European Championships but failed to get beyond the group stages in Euro 2000?

15. Denmark won the European Championships in 1992 after replacing which side in the final stages?

SOUTH AMERICAN INTERNATIONALS

1. Whose captained Brazil to the World Cup in 1970 after scoring a memorable goal in the final against Italy?

2. Which Brazilian goalkeeper of the 1990s won over 100 caps for his country?

3. Who scored twice for Argentina in the final when they won the World Cup for the first time in 1978?

4. Which South American country won the first ever World Cup in 1930?

5. Which famous player scored 48 goals for Brazil from 1975 to 1986?

6. Which South American side defeated Scotland 3–1 in the opening stages of the 1978 World Cup in Argentina?

7. Which Brazilian was voted Player of the Tournament in the 1994 World Cup in the USA?

8. Who is the only Argentinean to have scored more than 50 international goals?

9. Which South American country faced England for the only occasion in the 1986 World Cup finals?

10. Which player scored the only goal of the famous Brazil-England clash in the 1970 World Cup finals?

11. Which Colombian international, with a distinctive hairstyle, was voted South American Footballer of the Year in 1987?

12. Who was the 'chain-smoking' manager of the 1978 Argentinean World Cup side?

13. He was playing league football in Britain in 2001 and scored the only goal of the 1990 World Cup clash for Argentina against Brazil?

14. Which player appeared at Wembley for both Brazil and Arsenal in the 1999–2000 season?

15. Current player Vitor Barbosa Ferreira is better known as who?

QUICKFIRE

1. Who played in goal for Wales in the late 1990s but was born in Barnsley and played for Nottingham Forest?

2. Which Dutch player scored one of the World Cup's best goals in 1998 that eliminated Argentina at the quarter-final stage?

3. Who was the experienced goalkeeper who withdrew from the 1998 Scottish World Cup squad?

4. For which club did Andy Gray score the winning goal in a League Cup final?

5. Who, at the age of 40 years 92 days, is the oldest man to captain his country to World Cup success?

6. Who were the Cameroon brothers in the 1990 World Cup, one of whom scored the first goal of the competition, whilst the other was the first to be sent off?

7. Which Liverpool player in 1982 and 1987 was the last man to score in two League Cup finals?

8. Which manager took his side to six League Cup finals winning on four occasions?

9. For which country was Gilbert Dresch playing when he was sent off at Wembley against England in 1977?

10. Which legendary manager took his first managerial post in March 1960 with Dunfermline?

11. In the 2000–1 season which West Ham player became the first man to have been both Premiership Player and Manager of the Month?

12. Who was the goalkeeper beaten by the original 'Hand of God' in 1986?

13. Who has managed Spurs in an FA Cup final and also managed a team against Spurs in the final?

14. Alan Ashman was the manager of which 1960s FA Cup-winning side?

15. Which Wimbledon defender in the 1988 FA Cup final was the first Republic of Ireland international to be transferred for £2 million?

QUICKFIRE

1. Who was the Liverpool player who missed a penalty in the 2001 Worthington Cup final shoot-out?
2. Which club does television presenter Terry Christian support?
3. How does Hugh Dallas make a contribution to the game of football?
4. Who was sacked as coach to the England under-21 side in 1999?
5. Which country did England famously beat 9–3 at Wembley in April 1961?
6. Which British city was represented by two clubs in the same European Cup competition in 1968–69?
7. In 1981–2 Craig Madden established a record for most league goals in a season at which North West club?
8. Which club did Berwick Rangers knock-out of the Scottish Cup famously in 1967?
9. Which famous international, after replacing the injured Bobby Ferguson, saved a penalty for West Ham United against Stoke City in a League Cup semi-final replay in 1972?
10. Which former West Brom and Manchester Utd half-back was Jack Charlton's assistant in his time as the manager of Republic of Ireland?
11. Although born in Liverpool, in 1959 he was the first player capped by England with a Scottish club and later played in Italy – who is he?
12. Who was the Nigerian who made his debut for his country in November 1999 having just moved from Bristol City to Wolves for a fee of £3.5 million?
13. Which Division One side in the 2000–1 season are the only English team to have played FA Cup ties in all four home countries?
14. Who with Chelsea and Manchester United in the 1960s and 70s became the first manager to lose Wembley FA Cup finals with different clubs?
15. Which Manchester United defender was the PFA Player of the Year in 1992?

The Group phase

1. In 1970 Brazil kept the Jules Rimet Trophy after winning the World Cup three times – but which three sides did they beat in those finals?
(3 points)

2. Since 1990 which three players have been voted European Footballer of the Year whilst playing for Barcelona?
(3 points)

3. Which six players whose surnames begin with the letter 'C' have captained England in full internationals since 1960?
(6 points)

Penalty Shoot-out

1. Which player did Newcastle sign from Wimbledon for £7million in July 2000?

2. Which is the only city in England to stage top-flight football in the Football League since it started in 1888?

3. For which club was Kerry Dixon the Division Three leading scorer in 1982–83 with 26 goals prior to joining Chelsea?

4. Which England player in the 1962 World Cup final was on the books of an Italian club at the time?

5. Who in 1984 set a Scottish Premier League record when scoring five goals for Dundee United against Morton?

Full-time

In November 1971 Glasgow Rangers missed three penalties to lose a shoot-out against Sporting Lisbon in a Cup Winners Cup tie, after drawing 6–6 on aggregate. However the players and officials had forgotten that, as they had lost 4–3 in the second leg after winning the first game 3–2, then the Scottish side should have gone through on the recently-introduced away goals rule. Shortly afterwards UEFA awarded the tie to Rangers and suspended the Belgian ref.

'I asked the players who wanted to take a penalty and there was an awful smell coming from a few of them' – then-Millwall boss Mick McCarthy after his side beat Chelsea on penalties in the FA Cup in 1995

Several foreign clubs have the same name as English clubs. Arsenal (founded by supporters of the English club in Lesotho) won their country's league title in 1989 and 1991 to match the feat of their English namesakes.

The Group phase

1. Which four league grounds have staged FA Cup semi-
    finals on 17 or more occasions?
    (4 points)

2. Which four Spanish clubs reached the quarter-finals of the
    UEFA Cup in 2000–1?
    (4 points)

3. With which four clubs did Denis Law win Scotland caps
    from 1959 to 1974?
    (4 points)

Penalty Shoot-out

1. Who came on a goalkeeper for Aston Villa after just eight
    minutes of the 1982 European Cup final?

2. Later to play for Manchester United, who scored a
    Scottish Premiership record of 35 goals for Celtic in the
    1986–87 season?

3. When Andy Cole went to Manchester United from
    Newcastle in 1995 which winger went in the opposite
    direction ?

4. For which club did Ted McDougall score a record 42
    league goals in a season in 1971–72?

5. Who was the manager of West Ham United between 1961
    and 1974?

Full-time

The carrot connection:

In a 1998 Brazilian league game, Edmilson of Atletico Mineiro produced a carrot from his shorts after scoring in order to taunt fans of their opponents, America-Belo Horizonte, who were known as 'The Rabbits'!

Stuart Pearce on his chances of making the England squad: 'I can see the carrot at the end of the tunnel.'

Many comedians have aligned themselves with league clubs, most notably Jasper Carrott with Birmingham City. Other comedians include Mike Yarwood (Stockport), Jim Bowen (Morecambe) and Eric Morecambe (Luton Town).

BRITISH CLUBS

1. Who was the first foreigner to manage Arsenal?

2. Which snooker impresario do you associate with Leyton Orient?

3. Which forward was sold to Coventry in 1994 by Manchester United for £2 million after just four league games in two years for the Old Trafford club?

4. Later to be Glenn Hoddle's assistant with England, in 1993–94 John Gorman was in charge of which club who were relegated from the Premiership?

5. Of which club was the much-travelled manager Neil Warnock the boss in 2000–2001?

6. Which club beat Leeds United both home and away in the Champions Cup second group stage in the 2000–1 season?

7. Who gave away a penalty in Chelsea's defeat by Manchester United in the 1994 FA Cup final and then scored his club's second goal in the 1997 final?

8. Against which side did Roy Keane injure himself so badly in September 1997 that he missed the rest of the season?

9. Who in March 1996 moved from Manchester City to Blackburn and was sent off after only three minutes of his debut against Everton?

10. Who was sacked as manager of Celtic in 1994 after just eight months in charge after allegedly refusing to move to Scotland?

11. Who in August 1986 was sent off in his first game in charge of Rangers?

12. A villain of a FA Cup final incident, when he cynically fouled Paul Allen of West Ham, he played for both Arsenal and Tottenham during the 1970s – who is he?

13. Who was the manager sacked by Oldham in 1982 after spending 23 years at the club as player and manager?

14. Who in July 1986 was announced as the new Scotland manager although he had yet to manage a club?

15. For which Scottish club was Willie Struth the manager from 1920–1957?

BRITISH CLUBS

1. Which player scored a hat-trick on his full debut for
    Southampton against Arsenal in 1988 aged 17 years?

2. Which former Manchester United captain was appointed
    manager of Huddersfield in May 1999?

3. Which Liverpool defender scored two own goals in the
    first half against Manchester United in September 1999?

4. Which legendary manager was nickname 'Old Big 'Ead'?

5. Who is the current Sheffield Wednesday player was an
    England star of the 1990 World Cup in Italy?

6. Which British club in 1993–4 bought Basile Boli and
    Brian Laudrup for nearly £5 million?

7. Which Liverpool striker scored in ten successive First
    Division matches – the last game of 1986–7 and first nine
    of 1987–8?

8. In the mid-1990s Middlesbrough signed three Brazilians:
    Juninho, Emerson and who else?

9. During the Falklands conflict which Tottenham player
    played for Paris St Germain 'on loan'?

10. Which defender won 50 of his 61 caps at Sheffield
    Wednesday for Northern Ireland and later managed
    Blackpool?

11. Who was the Watford striker whose goal in the 1984 FA
    Cup semi-final prevented Plymouth from reaching the
    final?

12. Which Premiership club (in 2000–1) won the FA Cup for
    the only time when beating Newcastle United in 1911?

13. In 1989 Rangers were one game away from the treble
    when Gary Steven's back pass gave which Celtic player
    the chance to score the only goal of the Scottish Cup
    Final?

14. When Chelsea beat Manchester United (by 1–0) in both
    their league games in the 1993–94 season, which player
    scored both goals?

15. Which club would you associate with Cold Blow Lane?

WOLVERHAMPTON WANDERERS

1. Which player has scored the most league goals for Wolves with 250 in a career?

2. Who top scored for Wolves in 1999–2000 with 16 league goals before moving to Leicester in the close season?

3. Who became manager of Wolves in January 2001?

4. Which current TV pundit became the most expensive player in Britain when he moved to Molineux from Aston Villa in 1979?

5. Who managed the club from 1986–1994, guiding the club to Division One and to a Wembley victory in the Sherpa Van Trophy?

6. Who was the son of a famous Premiership manager who joined Wolves from Manchester United in January 1994?

7. Who came to the club in 1993–4 from Feyenoord and captained the side in 1995–96?

8. Who failed to win the League Cup with Liverpool but captained Wolves to that trophy in 1980?

9. Which famous Wolves player captained England a record 90 times during his 105 game international career?

10. Who became a manager for the 17th time when he took charge of the Midlands club in 1984–85?

11. Which goalkeeper made a club record 127 consecutive league appearances between 1970 and 1973?

12. Which Northern Ireland centre-forward played against the club in the 1960 FA Cup Final for Blackburn and later moved to Molineux?

13. He was the last amateur to play in a FA Cup Final and then went onto captain Wolves in the 1960 final, the same year as he was voted Footballer of the Year – who is he?

14. Who scored the winner in the 1974 League Cup final and won just one cap in for England in 1973 against Northern Ireland?

15. Who was capped by England before moving to Wolves, and captained the club to their 1974 League Cup Final victory?

WEST BROMWICH ALBION

1. Where do the club play their home games?

2. Who was the West Brom player who topped the Football League leading scorers' list 1998–9 with 31 goals?

3. Which England captain moved from Old Trafford to the Midland side in 1981 for a British record fee?

4. Who was the charismatic manager of the club when they finished third in Division One in 1978–9?

5. Which Irish international winger moved to Sunderland for £2.5 million in December 1999?

6. Paul Peschisolido scored 15 goals in 1996–97, but which country does the come from?

7. Who won three caps for England whilst at the club, then three more with Real Madrid where he played in a European Cup Final against Liverpool?

8. Who was the former Leeds player who became the club's player-manager in 1975?

9. Which club did WBA defeat by a single goal to win the 1968 FA Cup final?

10. What is the unusual nickname of the club besides 'Albion' and 'the Throstles?

11. Which former Albion player closed Skinner and Baddiel's TV show by singing?

12. Who in 1979 became the country's first £500,000 player when he left Middlesbrough and moved to Albion?

13. Which player scored a record 218 league goals for the club between 1963–1979?

14. Who was the Welsh full back who captained the side to their FA Cup final win in 1968?

15. Which centre forward – nicknamed 'Smokin' Joe' - scored for Albion on his debuts in each of five different competitions, and was capped by England although he was born in French Guyana?

THE CUPS – General

1. Which Division One side defeated Southampton 4–3 in the FA Cup fifth round in 2001 after being 3–0 down at half-time?

2. Which member of Arsenal's 1971 FA Cup-winning side would later manage the Gunners to victory in the final?

3. When Liverpool won the League Cup final at Wembley in 1983 who was their manager who collected the trophy in place of the captain Graeme Souness?

4. Steve Harper kept goal for which side in a FA Cup final during the 1990s?

5. Which Liverpool player in 1987 became the first man to appear in six League Cup finals?

6. Who scored twice for Manchester United when they beat Brighton in the 1983 FA Cup final replay?

7. Later Director of Football at White Hart Lane, in 1987 he was the Spurs manager for the FA Cup final?

8. What was the name of the trophy contested between 1970 and 1975 which was for clubs from England, Scotland, Northern Ireland and the Republic of Ireland who were not involved in Europe?

9. Which side knocked Manchester United out of the League Cup in the 2000–1 season by 2–1 in the fourth round?

10. Who was the 1975 PFA Young Player of the Year who played in goal for West Ham in the final in the same year?

11. Which player has scored goals at Wembley in the FA Cup semi-final for Spurs and a final for Everton?

12. Malcolm Crosby managed which club in a FA Cup final in the 1990s?

13. Which Republic of Ireland international appeared in major finals at Wembley for three different clubs in four seasons from 1983–86: Brighton, Liverpool and QPR?

14. Which current Premiership side's youth team won the FA Youth Cup in 1999 by defeating Coventry City 9–0 on aggregate?

15. Who managed Newcastle United in the 1976 League Cup final and then returned to the final with Everton twelve months later?

FA CUP – General

1. Who was the manager of Middlesbrough when they played Chelsea in the 1997 final?

2. Which Republic of Ireland international was on the losing side in FA Cup semi-finals with Southampton (1986), Norwich City (1989) and Aston Villa (1996)?

3. Which midfielder in the 1980s and 1990s became the first man to obtain four loser's medals in FA Cup finals at Wembley, three with Everton and one with Sunderland?

4. Who was the only player to appear in five finals during the 1990s, the first with Nottingham Forest in 1991 and then a further four with Manchester United?

5. Peter Rodrigues was the captain of which Cup-winning side of the 1970s?

6. For which club in 1970 did Marvin Hinton become the first substitute to appear in a FA Cup final and replay?

7. Who came on as a substitute for Manchester United in both the 1995 and 1996 finals?

8. Which man lifted the Cup as West Ham captain in both 1975 and 1980 and later managed the Hammers?

9. Which side, in Division One in the 2000–1 season, won three of the first seven FA Cup finals played at Wembley from 1923 onwards?

10. Which Fourth Division side produced one of the great FA Cup shocks by defeating the mighty Leeds United 3–2 in the fifth round in 1971?

11. Who played for Newcastle United against Liverpool in the 1974 final and in 1977 played for Liverpool in the final?

12. Who scored a rare penalty for Manchester City in the 1981 FA Cup final replay against Spurs?

13. Which legendary manager was the first to manage two different clubs to victory in the FA Cup final, Huddersfield in 1922 and Arsenal in 1930?

14. Whose 26–0 win over Hyde United in the FA Cup in 1887 remains the highest score by a side in any league or cup match in England?

15. Gary Brooke is the only player to appear as a substitute in three Wembley finals (including replays) – but for which side?

EUROPEAN CLUBS

1. Who scored twice for Manchester United in the 1968 European Cup final against Benfica?

2. Who scored for Fiorentina against both Arsenal and Manchester United in the European Cup in 1999–2000?

3. Who scored 47 goals for Benfica in the European Cup, only two behind the leading scorer Alfredo di Stefano?

4. For which club did Gianfranco Zola score 49 goals in Serie A?

5. For which French side did Fabien Barthez play before joining Manchester United in 2000?

6. Which Italian forward went from Atletico Madrid to Lazio in 1998 for £17.5 million and then moved to Inter Milan for £31 million twelve months later?

7. Which English side went out of the UEFA Cup 2–1 on aggregate to Kaiserslauten in the 1999–2000 season?

8. Which was the first club from outside the Iberian peninsula to win the European Cup?

9. Who when playing for Ajax won the European Golden Boot for the top league scorer in the 1985–86 season?

10. With which Spanish club was Ron Atkinson the manager during the 1988–89 season?

11. For which club did Johnny Rep score the only goal of a European Cup final?

12. Who was the Argentinean midfielder who moved from Parma to Lazio for £19.8 million in 1999?

13. Which Spanish side, who have never won a European trophy, knocked both Aston Villa and Liverpool out of the UEFA Cup in 1998–99?

14. For which Italian club did Guiseppe Bergomi make a record 117 appearances in European competitions up to 1998?

15. In which venue is the European Super Cup played each year?

BRITISH CLUBS IN EUROPE

1. Who became Aston Villa manager during the 1981–82 season when they went on to win the European Cup?

2. In the 1999–2000 UEFA Cup, which English side was beaten 1–0 on aggregate by Roma in the Third Round?

3. Who is the only manager to win European trophies with both English and Scottish clubs?

4. Which Italian side ended Norwich City's heroic run in the 1993–94 UEFA Cup, beating the Canaries 2–0 on aggregate in the third round?

5. Who was the manager of Celtic when they won the European Cup in 1967?

6. Who was the caretaker manager of Arsenal when they appeared in the 1995 European Cup Winners Cup Final?

7. He captained Liverpool to a European Cup final win and made his only appearance for Spurs in a UEFA Cup tie in Keflavik in 1971 – who is he?

8. Which English side recorded a 16–0 aggregate win over Lyn Oslo of Norway in the 1969–70 European Cup?

9. Which club have Arsenal and Spurs both beaten in European finals?

10. Currently in Divison Two of the Football League, they played two seasons in Europe in the UEFA Cup in 1972–73 and 1974–75 – who are they?

11. Which man made history in the 1990s by becoming the first player-manager to win a European trophy, doing so with an English club?

12. Barcelona in the 1958 Fairs Cup final beat a representative team from which English city?

13. Which English side is the only club to have played in European finals at both Wembley and Hampden Park?

14. Which club knocked both the holders Manchester United and Celtic on the way to winning the European Cup in 1969?

15. Which neutral city staged the Leeds United-Stuttgart replay in the 1992–93 European Cup after Stuttgart fielded an ineligible player in the match at Elland Road?

WORLD CUP – 1970s

1.   Which country staged the Finals in 1970?

2.   Which English referee awarded a penalty within two minutes of the start of the 1974 World Cup Final?

3.   Who replaced Gordon Banks in goal in the fateful match against West Germany in the 1970 finals?

4.   In 1978 Argentina defeated which country 6–0 in their final group match?

5.   Which country lost a memorable 1970 semi-final 4–3 to Italy after extra time?

6.   Who was the Scottish player sent home in disgrace after testing positive for a banned substance from Argentina in 1978?

7.   Which Brazilian scored in every game of the 1970 tournament, the only player ever to achieve this feat?

8.   Which Italian keeper conceded his first international goal in 19 hours of football against Haiti in the 1974 finals?

9.   In the 1978 World Cup which Argentinean star was described by John Motson as 'the ferret-faced little man'?

10. Which country recorded a memorable 1–0 win over the eventual champions West Germany in the 1974 group stages?

11. Who was the leading scorer in the 1970 tournament with ten goals?

12. Which country was eliminated from the 1978 tournament whilst remaining unbeaten in their seven matches?

13. Who by beating Mexico 3–1 in 1978 became the first African country to win a match in the finals?

14. Who was the Polish goalkeeper who saved a penalty in their crucial game against West Germany in the 1974 tournament?

15. Which German in 1970 made history by becoming the first to score in four different World Cup finals tournaments – having started in 1958?

WORLD CUP – 1990s

1. Which 39–year-old Scottish goalkeeper was the oldest player in the 1998 finals?

2. Who was the Italian who was the leading scorer in the 1990 finals with six goals?

3. Which side memorably knocked out the holders Germany in 1994 by 2–1 in the quarter finals?

4. Apart from Shearer and Owen which other player scored against Argentina in the penalty shoot-out in the 1998 finals?

5. Who was fouled a record 53 times in the 1990 finals – nearly twice as often as Paul Gascoigne?

6. Which South American striker scored hat-tricks in the 1994 and 1998 finals – the only player to have scored hat-tricks in different World Cups?

7. Who scored the Republic of Ireland's goal in their defeat of Italy in 1994?

8. What World Cup first was achieved when the USA and Switzerland drew 1–1 in their opening group match in Detroit in 1994?

9. Name either of the players sent-off in a controversial incident in the Holland-West Germany game in the 1990 finals?

10. Which Frenchman missed the 1998 final after being sent-off in the semi-final against Croatia?

11. Whose missed penalty for Italy in the shoot-out in the 1994 final gave Brazil the trophy for the fourth time?

12. Which Italian goalkeeper created a new record in the 1990 finals by going 517 mins without conceding a goal?

13. How did Mark Warren in 1998 become the first Englishman involved in a World Cup Final since Jack Taylor in 1974?

14. Which Celtic veteran captained Scotland in the 1990 finals?

15. In the 1994 tournament which country beat Belgium and Morocco to become the first Asian nation to qualify for the knock-out stages?

QUICKFIRE

1.   Who kept goal for Leeds when they won the League in 1991–2 and played for Arsenal in the European Cup in 2000–2001?

2.   Which Spurs player once had to wear a protective face-mask after a clash with Wimbledon's John Fashanu?

3.   Kenny Cunningham is which club's most capped player with over 30 caps for the Republic of Ireland?

4.   Who are 'the Cobblers' who play at the Sixfields Stadium?

5.   Which player scored in a record ten consecutive games for Arsenal in 1994?

6.   Danish international Allan Simonsen, the scorer of a European Cup final goal, signed for which England club in 1982–3?

7.   Which Bolton player, born in Liverpool, picked the Republic of Ireland ahead of England during the 1990s?

8.   Who was the Manchester City chairman who resigned in December 1993?

9.   Who was the last Southampton player to win a full England cap?

10. Who joined Barcelona for a world record £4.2 million in May 1982?

11. In the final game of the 1993–4 season, which club was relegated from the top flight after conceding a goal in the last minute at Chelsea?

12. Which club did Manchester United beat 5–4 on penalties in the 1993 Charity Shield?

13. Who in 1994–5, when playing for Fulham, became the first player to accumulate 61 disciplinary points since the points system began?

14. For what year's World Cup final stages did all four home countries fail to qualify for the first time?

15. Apart from Manchester City, for which other club did both Mike and Nicky Summerbee play?

QUICKFIRE

1. Who with 29 goals was the leading scorer in the First Division in 1999–2000 in all competitions for Manchester City?

2. Which Arsenal player in 1999–2000 scored in seven consecutive appearances in the Premiership?

3. Who was the manager of Crystal Palace in the 2000–1 season when they reached the League Cup semi-finals?

4. Which country knocked Argentina out of the 1994 World Cup in the second round by 3–2 before going out on penalties to Sweden in the next round?

5. Who started only 25 league games (plus eight as substitute) for Man Utd when they won the League in 1996–7 but still scored 18 goals?

6. Which Division One manager in the 2000–1 season did Graeme Souness bring to Rangers in 1986–87 from Atlanta in Italy?

7. Who is the only Sheffield Wednesday player to be honoured with the Player of the Year award?

8. Which Arsenal man was given a £3000 fine and a nine match ban in 1988–9 after breaking Southampton player Glenn Cockerill's jaw?

9. Who went from Watford to AC Milan in 1983 for £1 million, and then returned to Vicarage Road in 1984 for half that amount?

10. In 1984 who became the first England captain to score a hat trick in an international since 1909?

11. Which club at the start of the 1985–6 season began with 13 successive victories in Division Three?

12. Which club beat Selkirk 20–0 in the Scottish Cup first round in 1984–5?

13. Who was the 'Butcher of Bilbao' who was banned by the Spanish FA for 18 matches in 1983–4 for a terrible tackle on Maradona?

14. Who in March 2000 became the first outfield player in England to make 1000 senior appearances when playing for Rochdale?

15. Which great player, and future England boss, won championship winner's medals with Everton in 1939 and Arsenal in 1948 and 1953?

The Group phase

1. On which seven league grounds were matches staged in
    Euro 96 in England?
    (7 points)

2. Which two European countries have staged the World Cup
    finals on two occasions?
    (2 points)

3. Which three clubs in the Premiership in the 2000–1
    season have not appeared in any of the three major
    European competitions?
    (3 points)

Penalty Shoot-out

1. Which Premiership team won the Second Division in
    1988–89 with a record 99 points?

2. What 40–year-old artefact caused the postponement of a
    Sheffield United home game during the 1984–5 season?

3. Which goalkeeper made his 350th appearance for
    Sheffield Wednesday in March 2001 against Gillingham?

4. In which season, during the 1980s, did the Football
    League introduce three points for a win?

5. For which country did Hallvar Thoresen score a
    memorable World Cup qualifying goal against England in
    1981?

Full-time

In the 1992 FA Cup final the winners Liverpool, and the losers Sunderland, both received each other's medals at the end of the game and had to exchange them in the dressing room afterwards.

Eddie Bishop of Chester City, grabbing the mike, after his side were denied a penalty, when watching the match next to the tannoy announcer: 'Come on ref – open your eyes man!!'

The first player to score from the spot in a penalty shoot-out in England was George Best in 1970 for Manchester United against Hull in the 1970 Watney Cup.

The Group phase

1. Since 1960 which are the six sides, from outside the top
    flight, to have appeared in an FA Cup final?
    (6 points)

2. For which four league clubs has David Seaman played in
    his career?
    (4 points)

3. Who were the pair of strikers who scored 55 league goals
    between them for Newcastle United in the 1993–94
    season?
    (2 points)

Penalty Shoot-out

1. Which manager was given the Freedom of the City of
    Dublin in 1994?

2. Who was the much-travelled England striker who in 1994
    appeared for his seventh London club when moving from
    West Ham to Millwall?

3. For which player in 1984 did Cologne receive £100,000 in
    compensation after Aberdeen broke an agreement to sell
    him to the German side, selling him to Manchester United
    instead?

4. Which country had the most players (68 in total)
    appearing in the Champions Cup in the 2000–1 season?

5. Who scored the opening goal of Euro '96?

Full-time

Cambridge United are the only league club whose highest home attendance was set in a friendly match – the 14,000 who saw the game against Chelsea in May 1970 remains a record for the Abbey Stadium.

David Mellor on Radio 5 Live's *Six-O-Six* to Peterborough fan: 'That's great that you support them – sing us the Pompey Chimes.'

For many years it was recorded that Bryan Robson's goal after just 27 seconds against France in the1982 World Cup was the quickest in finals history. However further research by FIFA, years later, awarded that distinction to Vaclav Masek of Czechoslovakia, who scored 15 seconds from the start of the game against Mexico in the 1962 finals.

BRITISH CLUBS

1. Who captained Arsenal when they last achieved 'the Double'?

2. Which French international, also a member of Real Madrid's European Cup-winning side of 1998, played for Middlesbrough in 2000–2001?

3. Who was the former West Ham striker who scored both of Celtic's goals when they beat Dundee United by 2–1 in the 1988 Scottish Cup final?

4. What game is the traditional curtain raiser to the English season?

5. Which player moved from Newcastle to Spurs for a fee of over £2 million in the summer of 1988?

6. Which player was the leading scorer in Division One in 1974–5, with Newcastle, and in 1976–7 with Arsenal?

7. Who was the manager of Sheffield United when they were relegated from the Premiership in 1993–4?

8. Which London club do you associate with South Africa Road?

9. Which Scottish international moved to Liverpool in 1981 from Ayr United for £300,000 and played for the club throughout the decade?

10. Who managed Dundee United from November 1971 and stayed until his resignation in 1993?

11. Who was the secretary and then Director General of the Football League who was the founder of the League Cup?

12. Of which team was Bill Lambton the manager for just three days in 1959?

13. What was famously repainted during the Derby County and Manchester City league match in 1977?

14. Which club won the first of their two league titles in 1950–1?

15. Which Scottish club has the dubious distinction of conceding 100 goals in a Premiership season twice, in 1984–85 and 1987–88?

BRITISH CLUBS

1. Which former footballer was the star of the film *Lock, Stock andTwo Smoking Barrels*?

2. In March 1998, who scored the only goal when Arsenal defeated Manchester United 1–0 at Old Trafford in a crucial Premiership game?

3. Which current Premiership manager was Scotland's leading scorer in 1965–66 with 31 league goals whilst at Dunfermline?

4. Which prolific forward was the leading scorer in the English First Division on six occasions between 1959 and 1969?

5. Which current Division One side is nicknamed 'the Clarets' after the colour of their shirts?

6. What is the popular nickname of former Tranmere manager John Aldridge?

7. Who scored twice in the 1989 FA Cup final and played for Bradford City in the 2000–1 season?

8. Which Scottish Premiership side plays in the town of Perth at McDiarmid Park?

9. Which club, during the 1970s, was the last to win the league title in their first season after promotion from Division Two?

10. At which club did the twins Dean and David Holdsworth start their careers?

11. Which father and son combination saw the father play centre forward for Chelsea in the 1967 FA Cup final, and his son win 32 caps as centre forward for England in the 1980s?

12. What did Bert Turner do in a FA Cup in 1946 that was later repeated by players in the finals of 1981 and 1987?

13. Which was the first London club to win the League Cup?

14. Who was the Hearts captain who in 1986 became the third player to be sent off in a Scottish FA Cup Final?

15. Which former Liverpool captain was known as 'Crazy Horse'?

SOUTHAMPTON

1. Who is the only Southampton player to score 100 goals in the Premiership?

2. Which club changed their grey shirts at half time in a game at The Dell in April 1996?

3. Who left Coventry in August 1999 and scored a last minute goal for the club that knocked Liverpool out of the Worthington Cup in 1999–2000?

4. Just 12 days after securing the club's Premiership status in 1997 who resigned his position as manager?

5. Which Southampton player moved from Skonto Riga, Latvia, and top-scored for the club in 1999–2000?

6. In June 1998, Southampton received a record £7.5million for which player?

7. Which former player is now a top horse-racing trainer?

8. Southampton reached their only League Cup final in 1979 but lost 3–2 to which club?

9. Who was a member of England's World Cup squad in 1966 and played a staggering 713 games for the club?

10. Who managed the club for 18 years from 1955–73, leading them from Division Three to Division One, which is the second longest managerial reign in English football since the war?

11. Who ended the 1973–4 season as the First Division's leading scorer yet still saw the Saints relegated?

12. Who was the Yugoslavian defender who played in the 1979 League Cup final for the Saints?

13. Which Welsh ace netted 37 league goals for the club during 1966–67, half the total number of goals scored by Southampton that season?

14. Who broke a leg in a FA Cup semi-final against Liverpool in 1986 but later in his career joined the Anfield club?

15. Who is the former Aston Villa and Northern Ireland international who managed the club from 1985 to 1991?

PORTSMOUTH

1. Who is the former Chelsea coach who became the club's manager in 2001?
2. Who in 1996 bought the club for a reported £1 and became chairman, whilst also being coach of Australia?
3. Later to manage Aston Villa, he was the Pompey manager in 1989–90 – who is he?
4. Who is the goal-keeping legend, with over 600 league appearances for Portsmouth, who was awarded an MBE in 2000–2001?
5. Which World Cup winner of 1966 has managed both Southampton and Portsmouth?
6. In August 1997 this player was both Manchester City's record buy and Portsmouth's record sale at £3.5million, when moving between the two clubs – who was he?
7. Who left the club as manager in 2000 to pursue a legal battle?
8. Who was Jimmy Greaves' sidekick on ITV and had a spell as manager of Pompey?
9. Which future Pompey defender, who has made over 300 league appearances for the club, played for Worcester City at the age of 15years 88 days in a FA Cup game in 1987 – the youngest player in the history of the competition?
10. Who was capped for England whilst playing in Italy, France and Scotland, and won his first cap in 1984 with Portsmouth?
11. Who was the Pompey forward who was the leading scorer in Division Two when Portsmouth were promoted in 1986–7?
12. Who captained Brighton in the 1983 FA Cup final after joining the club in 1979 for a Portsmouth record fee received of £130,000?
13. In 1991–2 Portsmouth played a club record 59 games. Which Welsh international defender played in all those games without even being spoken to by a referee at any time?
14. Who was the former Ipswich and England striker who played for Pompey on the last occasion they played in the top flight, in 1987–8?
15. Who played a record 764 league games for the club from 1946 to 1965?

THE CUPS – General

1. Which First Division club lost in the semi-finals of both major cup competitions in England in 1999–2000?

2. Which side was beaten 6–2 on aggregate by Liverpool in their 2000–1 League Cup semi-final?

3. Who scored the only goal of the 1976 FA Cup final when Southampton defeated Manchester United?

4. Who were the last pair of brothers to appear in a FA Cup-winning side?

5. Which Spurs forward scored a League Cup record 12 goals in a season in 1986–87?

6. In 1988–89 who became the first side to win two major Wembley finals in the same season?

7. Roy Dwight, who scored in the 1959 FA Cup final for Nottingham Forest as well as breaking his leg, is the uncle of which famous singer?

8. Which current Premiership club has appeared in FA Cup matches at Wembley in three consecutive seasons under three different managers?

9. Which side, which has now joined the league, was the last non-league club to reach the fifth round of the FA Cup, doing so in 1994?

10. Which Everton player in the 1984 FA Cup final, and Crystal Palace player in the 1990 final, had exactly the same name?

11. Which Leeds was sent-off in the Charity Shield at Wembley in 1974 against Liverpool?

12. Who scored Manchester United's winning goal in the 1990 FA Cup final?

13. What was significant in FA Cup history about Everton's 1–0 win over Liverpool in their fifth round second replay in February 1991?

14. Which club won the FA Youth Cup every year from 1953–57 inclusive?

15. Who was the QPR captain who missed the 1982 FA Cup final through suspension?

THE FA CUP – prior to 1970

1. Which club won the first FA Cup final at Wembley in 1923, defeating West Ham United 2–0?

2. Who scored a hat-trick for Blackpool against Bolton in the 1953 final, the only one scored at Wembley?

3. Who captained West Ham when they won the FA Cup final against Preston in 1964?

4. What appeared on players' shirts for the first time in the final when Everton played Manchester City in 1933?

5. Which venue staged the FA Cup final every year from 1895 to 1914?

6. He later managed Leeds United to FA Cup glory and played for Manchester City when they won the Cup in 1956 – who is he?

7. Which Scottish international was the only player to appear in all three of Spurs' FA Cup final victories of the 1960s, captaining them in the 1967 final?

8. Who kept goal for Leicester City when they lost in the finals of 1961 and 1963?

9. What were the names of the Chilean brothers who appeared for Newcastle United in the 1952 final?

10. Which side in 1927 is the only club to have taken the FA Cup out of England, by beating Arsenal 2–0 in the final?

11. Which famous England test batsman played with his brother in the Arsenal side that beat Liverpool 2–0 in the 1950 FA Cup final?

12. Which player scored in Newcastle United's final victories of both 1951 and 1955?

13. Who was the manager of the great Wolves side when they won the FA Cup in both 1949 and 1960?

14. Which venue staged the very first FA Cup final between The Wanderers and the Royal Engineers in 1872?

15. Which current Premiership side won the FA Cup in 1901 to become the last side to win the final whilst playing non-league football?

MANCHESTER UNITED IN EUROPE

1. Who was the manager of Manchester United when they won a European trophy for the first time?
2. Who played for Manchester United in the 1999 Champions League final, having appeared in the Gothenburg side that had eliminated United from the competition four years earlier?
3. Which player scored a record 28 goals for United in Europe from 1963 to 1969?
4. Who kept goal for United in their 1991 Cup Winners Cup final triumph?
5. When they went out of the Champions League in 1999–2000 in the quarter-final against Real Madrid, which United player scored an own goal at Old Trafford?
6. Who captained United when they won the Cup Winners Cup in 1991?
7. Which side did Manchester United play in the Champions League competition six times in three consecutive seasons from 1996–1999?
8. Which current player's first goal for United in Europe came against Galatasaray in 1994?
9. In the 1983–84 Cup Winners Cup quarter-final, against which side did United claw back a 2–0 first leg deficit to win the second 3–0 at Old Trafford?
10. In 1997 United reached the semi-finals of the European Cup for the first time since 1969, but lost on away goals to which side?
11. Which Turkish side in 1996 inflicted United's first ever defeat in a European tie at Old Trafford?
12. Which Belgian side did United beat 10–0 in their first European tie in 1956?
13. Who captained United in their European Cup final win of 1999?
14. Who scored twice for United when they beat Inter Milan in the first leg of their quarter-final tie in the 1998–99 European Cup?
15. Which Portugese side inflicted United's heaviest European defeat by 5–0 in the Cup Winners Cup in 1963–4?

LIVERPOOL IN EUROPE

1. Who was Liverpool's manager on the last occasion they won the European Cup?

2. Who captained Liverpool to victory in the 1981 European Cup final and is now assistant to Gerard Houllier at Anfield?

3. How many times have Liverpool won the European Cup?

4. In which year did Liverpool win the European Cup for the first time?

5. Which side did Liverpool play in the semi-finals of the UEFA Cup in 2000–1?

6. Whose first hat-trick in Europe for Liverpool was against Benfica in 1984 in the European Cup?

7. Which Welsh international scored nine goals for Liverpool in the UEFA Cup in the 1991–92 season, the most by any player in the competition that year?

8. Whose famous goal, after coming on as a substitute, won the quarter-final tie against Saint Etienne of France in the 1976–77 European Cup?

9. Which Scottish international scored two hat-tricks for Ipswich in their UEFA Cup campaign in 1980–1 and a hat-trick for Liverpool against Lech Poznan in the 1984–5 European Cup?

10. Who scored a memorable goal for Liverpool against Celtic in the UEFA Cup at Parkhead in 1997 after running from deep inside his own half?

11. Who scored six goals in Europe, consisting of two hat-tricks against Oulun and CSKA Sofia in the 1980–1 European Cup campaign?

12. In the 2000–1 UEFA Cup which player scored for Liverpool in the away leg in each of the first three rounds of the competition?

13. Which future manager of the Reds played in just one European game for the club, against Hibernian in 1970?

14. Who were the Scottish champions beaten 5–0 on aggregate by Liverpool in the 1980–1 European Cup?

15. Who was the England international who scored in their defeat by Borussia Dortmund in the 1966 European Cup Winners Cup final?

WORLD CUP - GENERAL

1.   Which country won the World Cup for the first time in 1954?

2.   In the 1966 World Cup which venue, not used in league football, staged games in the tournament?

3.   Prior to France in 1998, who had been the last host country to win the trophy?

4.   Who scored for Brazil in the Finals of 1958 and 1970?

5.   Which South American country staged the tournament in 1962?

6.   For which country did Antonio Carbajal play a then-record 21 games in the finals from 1950 to 1966?

7.   Which country were the first to win the trophy twice, doing so in 1934 and 1938?

8.   Who was the triumphant manager of Germany when they won the trophy in 1974?

9.   Who scored four times for Portugal when they came from behind to defeat North Korea 5–3 at Goodison Park in the 1966 quarter-finals?

10. Which European country, in the 1994 tournament, won their first match in the final stages after 17 games when defeating Greece?

11. What was the name of the stadium that staged the 1998 World Cup Final?

12. Which country last reached the World Cup semi-finals in 1970 when they lost 3–1 to Brazil?

13. Which European country inflicted Brazil's first World Cup defeat in 12 years by 3–1 in the group stages in 1966?

14. Which was the first country to have a player sent-off in the Final itself?

15. Which is the only country to have played all four British countries in the finals?

ENGLAND

1. Who won a record 78 games whilst in charge of England?

2. Who was the youngest player to appear for England in the 20th century?

3. Which player made his England debut in a 4–0 win over Peru in Lima in May 1962 and his last against Italy 11 years later?

4. Who was the first Englishman to win 100 caps for his country?

5. Who was the England's leading scorer of the 1960s with 42 goals in the decade?

6. Which country did England beat 8–0 in both home and away matches during the 1980s?

7. Who was the Chelsea striker whose four goals for England came in consecutive matches against West Germany and the USA in the summer of 1985?

8. Which Manchester United player made his England debut at Old Trafford against South Africa in May 1997?

9. Which striker made his first four appearances for England, from 1995–99, under four different managers?

10. Which full-back was included in England's World Cup squads of 1982 and 1986 but did not play a single match in the finals?

11. Against which of the British home countries did Kevin Keegan make his first three appearances for England?

12. Whose first two goals for England came against Luxembourg in the 6–0 win at Wembley in September 1999?

13. Which current Premiership keeper gave a man-of-the-match performance on his England debut against Brazil in Washington in June 1993?

14. Who was the only player to appear for England in their first match of the 1980s (Republic of Ireland, February 1980) and the last (Yugoslavia, December 1989)?

15. Against Holland in 1988, who became the last England player to score at both ends in an international?

QUICKFIRE

1. In what country were the 1992 European Championships held, memorably won by Denmark?

2. Which England international moved from Nottingham Forest to Aston Villa in March 1999 for £5.5 million?

3. Who was appointed manager of Nottingham Forest in 1975 as a successor to Allan Brown?

4. Who scored a record 199 league goals in a career for Manchester United?

5. Which club, which has appeared in the Premiership, plays home matches at the County Ground?

6. For which club did Ralph Coates score the winning goal in the 1973 League Cup final?

7. Which left-sided player for the Republic of Ireland is believed to be the only player to have scored direct from corner kicks on two occasions in internationals?

8. Later to manage Wales, he won 44 caps for the country from 1962 to 1975 whilst with Blackburn Rovers and Spurs – who is he?

9. Which club were runners-up in Division One on five occasions between 1965 and 1972?

10. Who was voted the World Footballer of the Year in 1996 and 1997?

11. Who was appointed player-manager of Portsmouth, for a temporary period, during the 2000–1 season?

12. Which Aston Villa forward was voted PFA Young Player of the Year in 1981?

13. Which Premiership club, in the 2000–1 season, won the first of their two league titles in 1936–37?

14. Where did Wales play their crucial 'home' World Cup qualifier against Scotland in 1977?

15. Which was the only club during the 1990s to be runner-up in both the league and FA Cup in the same season?

QUICKFIRE

1. Which Welsh club plays at the Racecourse Ground?

2. Which full-back, who won over 80 caps with England, scored his only international goal against Finland in 1984?

3. Which side was docked two league points following an infamous 20–man brawl at Old Trafford in 1990?

4. During the 1980s, which was the first side from Eastern Europe to win the European Cup?

5. What trophy did England, and two other countries, compete for at the end of each season from 1988 to 1991?

6. Which colourful character, and much-travelled manager, was appointed Scotland manager on 12 September 1971?

7. Rangers broke the Scottish transfer record in October 1968 when they bought which player from Hibernian for £100,000?

8. Who was the Manchester United full-back of the 1970s who played county cricket for Yorkshire and in 1985 played for England in an Ashes Test?

9. Which club won the Scottish League Cup in 1971–72, after a shock 4–1 over Celtic, to take their first trophy in over 50 years?

10. Which TV pundit in August 1995 said 'You can't win anything with kids'?

11. Who kept goal for Juventus in both their 1997 and 1998 European Cup finals and was then transferred to Inter Milan for £10.5 million, a record fee for a goalkeeper, in 1999?

12. Who was the former Tottenham player whose real name is Mohammed Ali Amar, and who scored a famous goal in a European Cup Winners Cup final?

13. Which overseas player won a League Championship with Arsenal in 1991 and the FA Cup with Everton in 1995?

14. The Tottenham 'Famous Five' in 1994–5 were Klinsmann, Sheringham, Anderton, Barmby and which Romanian striker?

15. Which French club won the Intertoto Cup in 1995–6 and then reached the UEFA Cup final when they lost to Bayern Munich?

The Group phase

1. Which six clubs have appeared in the semi-finals of the League Cup on seven or more occasions?
    (6 points)

2. Which four countries in Euro 2000 had squads that did not contain an English Premier League player?
    (4 points)

3. Which two Premiership clubs, in the 2000–1 season, have both won the old Second Division on a record six occasions?
    (2 points)

Penalty Shoot-out

1. Which England international was born in Chester on 14 December 1979?

2. Which North West side have played over 70 seasons in the English top flight without ever winning the title?

3. Which future Scottish manager was born in Lanarkshire in July 1940?

4. Who was the manager of the Tottenham 'double' winning side of 1961?

5. With which club was Trevor Senior the leading scorer in league football in the 1983–4 season with 36 league goals?

Full-time

The greatest number of penalties missed by one individual in a single game is the three by Martin Palermo for Argentina against Colombia in 1999. Hamilton Ricard also missed for Colombia in the same match.

Advert in local newspaper: 'Grazing land for sale, approx. 5 acres, houses 11 donkeys.' When potential buyers phoned up they discovered that the contact number given was Portsmouth FC.

The last attendance of over 70,000 for a league game in England was when 72,488 saw Everton play Liverpool at Goodison Park in September 1962.

The Group phase

1. Which three countries have appeared in the final of the
    European Championships on just one occasion?
    (3 points)

2. Which five clubs, not in the Premiership for the 2000–1
    season, have won the League Championship since 1945?
    (5 points)

3. For which four London clubs did Terry Venables play
    during his career?

Penalty Shoot-out

1. Which TV pundit won eight League Championship
    winners medals with Liverpool from 1979 to 1990?

2. Which England international was born in Gateshead on 27
    May 1967?

3. In 1978–9 Ross Jenkins was the league's leading scorer
    with 29 goals, but for which side was he playing?

4. Which England forward won League Championship
    medals with Manchester City in 1968 and Derby County
    in 1975?

5. Who captained AC Milan to victory in the 1963 European
    Cup final and managed Italy in the 1998 World Cup
    finals?

Full-time

Arsenal reached the FA Cup finals of 1971 and 1972 despite being away from home in every round in both seasons. Manchester United matched this in 1990 when they won the FA Cup without playing a single game at Old Trafford, and also did not play a Saturday game in the Cup until the final.

'Dave Challinor of Tranmere throws the ball further than I go on my holidays' – Ron Atkinson

When was the last time you saw Norwich City playing in their away kit? If they ever have to change their colours then the team's away kit is apparently all-white.

SOCCER BRAIN

Answers

MATCH 1 — Round 1

Player A
1. Arsenal
2. Crystal Palace
3. Ian Rush
4. Crystal Palace
5. Howard Wilkinson
6. Ipswich Town
7. Les Ferdinand
8. Watford
9. Denis Law
10. Gillingham
11. Alan Ball
12. Jim Leighton
13. Brian Deane
14. Stoke City
15. Q.P.R

Player B
1. Tony Cottee
2. Barry Fry
3. Green
4. Alan Shearer
5. Swindon Town
6. The 'Guvnor'
7. Sunderland
8. Leeds Utd
9. John Lukic
10. Dean Saunders
11. Nottingham Forest
12. Colin Clarke
13. Cardiff City
14. Arsenal 1993
15. Tunji Banjo/John Chiedozie

MATCH 1 — Round 2

Player A
1. Mick McCarthy
2. Paolo Wanchope
3. Denis Law
4. Niall Quinn
5. Uwe Rosler
6. Gillingham
7. Steve Coppell
8. Francis Lee
9. David White
10. Roger Palmer
11. Vienna
12. Huddersfield
13. Colin Bell
14. The Brightwells
15. W.B.A

Player B
1. Real Madrid
2. Benfica
3. Bryan Robson
4. PSV Eindhoven
5. Paul Ince
6. Mark Bosnich
7. Arnold Muhren
8. Peter Beardsley
9. Denis Irwin
10. Remi Moses
11. Spurs
12. Juninho
13. Mark Robins
14. Bryan Robson
15. Martin Buchan

MATCH 1 — Round 3

Player A
1. Arsenal
2. Thursday
3. Sheffield United
4. Kevin Ratcliffe
5. Kevin Moran
6. Man United
7. First by a substitute
8. Darren Anderton
9. David Harvey
10. Brighton
11. 2nd time beaten in Cup that season
12. Bert Trautmann
13. Danny Blanchflower
14. Bobby Robson
15. Andy Linighan

Player B
1. Brian McClair

2. Lawrie Sanchez
3. Trevor Francis
4. Ronnie Whelan
5. Stamford Bridge
6. John Aldridge
7. Gordon Smith
8. Roland Nilsson
9. Andy Gray
10. Liverpool
11. Emile Heskey
12. Nottingham Forest
13. Swindon Town
14. Chris Woods
15. Peter McParland

MATCH 1 Round 4

Player A
1. Real Madrid
2. Bobby Charlton
3. Joe Fagan
4. Juventus
5. Chris Waddle
6. Mike Newell
7. Ruud Gullit
8. Spartak Moscow
9. Derby County
10. Hamburg
11. France
12. Alfredo di Stefano
13. Phil Neal
14. Belgrade
15. Benfica

Player B
1. Nottingham Forest
2. Karl Heinz Reidle
3. David Batty
4. Andy Cole
5. Gianluca Vialli
6. Ally McCoist
7. Saint Etienne
8. Rome
9. Teddy Sheringham
10. Milan
11. Spain (in 2000)
12. Juup Heynckes
13. Marseilles

14. Faustino Asprilla
15. Dundee

MATCH1 Round 5

Player A
1. Joe Mercer
2. Peter Beardsley
3. Peter Shilton
4. France
5. Germany
6. Malcolm McDonald
7. Robert Lee
8. Steve Hodge
9. Scotland
10. Michael Owen
11. Stadium of Light
12. Argentina
13. San Marino
14. Dion Dublin
15. Phil Parkes

Player B
1. France
2. Argentina
3. Pele
4. Steve Foster
5. Holland
6. Franz Beckenbauer
7. Zaire
8. Chile
9. Toto Schillachi
10. Holland
11. Craig Burley
12. Gerry Armstrong
13. Italy
14. Teofilo Cubillas
15. Oman Biyik

MATCH 1 Round 6

Player A
1. Jan Molby
2. Brighton
3. Ally McCoist
4. Darlington
5. Latics
6. Alan Ball

7. Niall Quinn
8. Nuno Gomes
9. Wycombe Wanderers
10. Luc Nilis
11. Ipswich Town
12. Chris Kamara
13. Arsenal
14. Hampden Park
15. Sol Campbell

Player B
1. Didier Deschamps
2. Alan Hansen
3. Exeter City
4. Nick Barmby
5. Andrei Kanchelskis
6. Tom Finney
7. Sammy McIlroy
8. Anfield
9. Steffan Freund
10. Gary Lineker
11. Stephen Clemence
12. Peter Shilton
13. Wrexham
14. Basile Boli
15. Gordon Durie

MATCH 1
The Group Phase

Player A
1. Everton
    Blackburn Rovers
    Aston Villa
2. Jesper Olsen
    Jan Molby
    John Jensen
    Peter Schmiechel
    Jakob Kjeldberg
    Mikkel Beck
3. Rodney
    Danny
    Ray

Penalty Shoot-out
1. Rigobert Song
2. Bobby Moore
3. Burnley

4. Paul Ince
5. Manchester United

Player B
1. Bari
    Sampdoria
    Juventus
2. Kuwait
    Morocco
    Egypt
    Cameroon
    Tunisia
3. Aston Villa
    Sheffield Wednesday
    Coventry City
    Nottingham Forest

Penalty Shoot-out
1. Emlyn Hughes
2. Bury
3. Tommy Lawton
4. Millwall
5. Nick Barmby

MATCH 2   Round 1

Player A
1. Barnsley
2. Burnley
3. Ian Rush
4. Roy Keane
5. Brian Kidd
6. Manchester City
7. Preston North End
8. John Toshack
9. Mark Lawrenson
10. AC Milan
11. Geoff Hurst
12. Graeme Souness
13. Bournemouth
14. Jurgen Klinsmann
15. Stoke City

Player B
1. Mike Walker
2. Stoke City
3. Gillingham
4. Ian Wright
5. Bobby Robson
6. Ipswich Town
7. Kenny Dalglish
8. Terry Venables
9. Tommy Docherty
10. John King
11. West Ham United
12. Paul Warhurst
13. He was the white police horse
14. Sheffield United
15. Crewe

MATCH 2   Round 2

Player A
1. Danny Murphy
2. Robbie Fowler
3. Leeds United
4. Bolton
5. John Aldridge
6. Joe Fagan
7. Nick Barmby
8. Fulham
9. Graeme Souness
10. Jamie Carragher
11. Ian Callaghan
12. Gary Gillespie
13. Ronnie Rosenthal
14. Everton
15. Phil Neal

Player B
1. Tranmere Rovers
2. Archie Knox
3. Andrei Kanchelskis
4. Kevin Ratcliffe
5. Neville Southall
6. Tony Cottee
7. Peter Reid
8. Richard Gough
9. Martin Keown
10. Howard Kendall
11. Olivier Dacourt
12. Maurice Johnston
13. Joe Royle
14. Bob Latchford
15. Colin Harvey

MATCH 2   Round 3

Player A
1. Leeds United
2. Bill Shankly
3. Ian Porterfield
4. Ron Harris
5. Frank McLintock
6. Steve Heighway
7. Sammy McIlroy
8. Peter Osgood
9. Peter Taylor
10. Ted McDougall
11. Mick Jones
12. Wolves
13. Stamford Bridge
14. 1975
15. Blyth Spartans

Player B
1. Alex Ferguson
2. Anglo-Italian Cup
3. Kingstonian

4. Wimbledon
5. Newcastle United
6. Stoke City
7. Paul Gascoigne
8. Watney Cup
9. Gary Stevens
10. QPR
11. Oldham Athletic
12. Bryan Robson
13. Ron Atkinson
14. Gary O'Reilly
15. Leicester City

MATCH 2   Round 4

Player A
1. Alan Smith
2. Gordon Strachan
3. Liverpool
4. Cardiff City
5. Anderlecht
6. Gianluca Vialli
7. Wrexham
8. Bobby Robson
9. Arnold Muhren
10. Dan Petrescu
11. Rangers
12. Alan Simonsen
13. Peter Osgood
14. Hamburg
15. Hans Krankl

Player B
1. Spain
2. Juventus
3. Alan Kennedy
4. Panathaniakos
5. Sturm Graz
6. Porto
7. Jimmy Armfield
8. Tommy Gemmell
9. Borussia Dortmund
10. Barcelona
11. Kenny Dalglish
12. Nicolas Anelka
13. John Pierre Papin
14. Marco Van Basten
15. Frank Gray

MATCH 2   Round 5

Player A
1. Teddy Sheingham
2. Patrik Berger
3. Les Ferdinand
4. Alan Shearer
5. Karel Poborsky
6. Berti Vogts
7. Gary Neville
8. Andy Goram
9. Andreas Kopke
10. Jordi Cruyff
11. Jamie Redknapp
12. Only goal via free-kick
13. Steve Stone
14. Udinese
15. Gianfranco Zola

Player B
1. Romania
2. Denmark
3. Patrick Kluivert
4. Sylvain Wiltord
5. Holland
6. Steve Gerrard
7. Dino Zoff
8. Frank de Boer
9. Nigel Martyn
10. Magnus Hedman
11. Abel Xavier
12. Slovenia
13. Hakan Sukur
14. Graham Poll
15. Roger Lemerre

MATCH 2   Round 6

Player A
1. Brighton
2. Duncan Ferguson
3. Preston
4. Jimmy Glass
5. Italy
6. Gary Lineker
7. John McGinlay
8. Nottingham Forest
9. Robbie Fowler

10. Roy Keane
11. England
12. Clarence Seedorf
13. Manchester United
14. Uli Steilike
15. Chelsea

Player B
1. Brentford
2. West Ham
3. Alex Ferguson
4. Wimbledon
5. David Pleat
6. Liverpool
7. Gary Stevens
8. Ronald Koeman
9. Eusebio
10. Brian McClair
11. Sheffield United
12. Chris Bart-Williams
13. Chris Waddle
14. Bailey (Roy and Gary)
15. Clive Thomas

MATCH 2
The Group Phase

Player A
1. George Cohen
   Nobby Stiles
   Martin Peters
2. Andy Cole
   Fabien Barthez
   Henning Berg
   Jaap Stam
   Dwight Yorke
3. Jimmy Greaves
   Steve Archibald
   Clive Allen
   Gary Lineker

Penalty Shoot-out
1. Koeman (Erwin and Ronald)
2. Grimsby
3. Celtic
4. David Batty
5. Ron Greenwood

Player B
1. John Toshack
   Mike Smith
   Bobby Gould
2. Terry Butcher
   Paul Gascoigne
   Gary Stevens
   Trevor Steven
   Mark Hateley
   Chris Woods
3. Jim Smith
   Graham Taylor
   Brian Clough

Penalty Shoot-out
1. Germany
2. David Kelly
3. Luton Town
4. First players sent-off in final
5. Julian Dicks

MATCH 3   Round 1

Player A

1. Cole (Andy, Ashley and Joe)
2. David Beckham
3. Paul Rideout
4. The Victoria Ground
5. Kidderminster Harriers
6. Tommy Docherty
7. Wimbledon
8. Kevin Keegan
9. Southampton
10. Mike and Ian Walker
11. Peter Shilton
12. Arsenal
13. Steve Bull
14. Mark Chamberlain
15. Wolves

Player B

1. Birmingham City
2. Wembley
3. Bobby Robson
4. Paolo di Canio
5. Liverpool
6. Dario Gradi
7. David Beasant
8. Kenny Daglish
9. Watford
10. Oldham Athletic
11. Tony Waddington
12. Chelsea
13. Jimmy Quinn
14. Dundee United
15. Glasgow Rangers

MATCH 3   Round 2

Player A

1. Sol Campbell
2. Gary Mabbutt
3. Allan Nielsen
4. Coventry City
5. Tim Sherwood
6. Clive Allen
7. Justin Edinburgh
8. Tony Parkes

9. Pat Jennings
10. Keith Burkinshaw
11. Teddy Sheringham
12. Wimbledon
13. Danny Blanchflower
14. Bristol Rovers
15. Les and Clive Allen

Player B

1. Robert Pires
2. Davor Suker
3. Ian Wright
4. Nicolas Anelka
5. Terry Neill
6. Charlie Nicholas
7. Alan Smith
8. David Platt
9. David O'Leary
10. Tony Woodcock
11. Kanu
12. Loughborough
13. Stuart Houston
14. Tony Adams
15. Manchester United

MATCH 3   Round 3

Player A

1. Crystal Palace
2. Paul Gascoigne
3. Brian Little
4. Steve McManaman
5. Tony Cottee
6. Swindon Town
7. Ray Clemence
8. Chris Woods
9. John Sheridan
10. Liverpool lost when Rush scored
11. Steve Morrow
12. Rodney Marsh
13. Les Sealey
14. Stockport County
15. Ray Graydon

Player B

1. Frank Stapleton
2. Ricky Villa

3. Clive Allen
4. Liverpool
5. Bobby Gould
6. Steve Foster
7. 1986 Liverpool v Everton
8. John Lyall
9. Dave Beasant
10. Tommy Hutchison
11. Steve Perryman
12. Keith Houchen
13. Nottingham Forest
14. Ronnie Whelan
15. Jimmy Case

MATCH 3   Round 4

Player A
1. Moved from two legs to one-off final
2. Faustino Asprilla
3. Leicester City
4. Michael Owen
5. Martin Chivers
6. Nottingham Forest
7. Careca
8. Real Madrid
9. Inter Milan
10. Kevin Gallacher
11. Ray Parlour
12. Spurs
13. Ivan Zamorano
14. Denis Law
15. Juup Heynckes

Player B
1. Sporting Lisbon
2. Sampdoria
3. Marco Van Basten
4. Munich 1860
5. PSV Eindhoven
6. Fiorentina
7. Juventus
8. Gerard Houllier
9. Dinamo Kiev
10. Atletico Madrid
11. Istanbul
12. Belgium
13. Borussia Dortmund

14. Denmark
15. Uwe Seeler

MATCH 3   Round 5

Player A
1. Marcel Desailly
2. Dino Zoff
3. Germany
4. Australia
5. Liberia
6. Egypt
7. Cameroon
8. Slaven Bilic
9. Missed three penalties
10. Brazil
11. Ferenc Puskas
12. Andrei Kanchelskis
13. Norway
14. Super Eagles
15. Vava

Player B
1. Terry Yorath
2. Alex McLeish
3. Michael Hughes
4. Leeds United
5. Wales
6. Laurie McMenemy
7. Leighton James
8. Paul McStay
9. Yugoslavia
10. Romania
11. Davie Cooper
12. Mal Donaghy
13. John Charles
14. Steve Archibald
15. Terry Neill

MATCH 3   Round 6

Player A
1. Chris Sutton
2. Southport
3. Dean Saunders
4. Rigobert Song
5. Chelsea
6. York City

7.	Terry Paine	3.	Juventus
8.	Nick Henry	4.	Ole Gunnar Solskjaer
9.	Millwall	5.	Spurs
10.	Jan Domarski		

7. Terry Paine
8. Nick Henry
9. Millwall
10. Jan Domarski
11. Denmark
12. Titi Camara
13. Gordon Banks
14. Galatasaray
15. Manchester United

Player B
1. Michael Owen
2. Les Ferdinand
3. Middlesbrough
4. Paul Scholes
5. Roberto Di Matteo
6. Alun Armstrong
7. Blackburn Rovers
8. Holdsworth (David and Dean)
9. Gunnar Halle
10. Yugoslavia
11. Chelsea
12. Peter Shilton (son is Sam)
13. Neil Redfearn
14. Sir Alf Ramsey
15. Terry Venables

MATCH 3
The Group Phase

Player A
1. Jurgen Klinsmann
   Eric Cantona
   Gianfranco Zola
   Dennis Bergkamp
   David Ginola
2. Bruce Grobbelaar
   Steve Nicol
   Ian Rush
3. Crystal Palace
   Nottingham Forest
   Bolton
   Middlesbrough

Penalty Shoot-out
1. Gary Lineker
2. Kevin Sheedy

3. Juventus
4. Ole Gunnar Solskjaer
5. Spurs

Player B
1. Saint Etienne
   Marseille
   Monaco
   Nantes
2. Barnet
   Wycombe Wanderers
   Macclesfield Town
   Cheltenham Town
   Kidderminster Harriers
3. David Platt
   Alan Shearer
   Stuart Pearce

Penalty Shoot-out
1. Teddy Sheringham
2. Sammy Lee
3. Trevor Francis
4. Arsenal
5. Lee Sharpe

MATCH 4   Round 1

Player A
1. Seth Johnson
2. Bristol City
3. New Order
4. Dennis Bergkamp
5. Wigan Athletic
6. Luther Blissett
7. Brian Clough
8. Pools Panel
9. Graham Taylor
10. Ipswich Town
11. John Bailey
12. Dion Dublin
13. Paolo Maldini
14. Michael Owen
15. Tomas Brolin

Player B
1. Burnley
2. Chris Waddle
3. Chris Armstrong
4. Andy Gray
5. Wimbledon
6. Brighton
7. Newcastle United
8. Bob Wilson
9. Bobby Robson
10. Ipswich Town
11. Arsenal
12. Tony Adams
13. Mario Kempes
14. Dean Saunders
15. Rio/Les Ferdinand

MATCH 4   Round 2

Player A
1. Andy Cole
2. John Barnes
3. Shay Given
4. Alan Shearer
5. Steve Watson
6. Ossie Ardiles
7. David Ginola
8. Sheffield Wednesday
9. Dietmar Hamann
10. Mirandinha
11. Ujpest Dosza
12. Jackie Milburn
13. Wimbledon
14. The Robledos
15. Jack Charlton

Player B
1. Frederick Kanoute
2. Roker Park
3. Watford
4. Stefan Schwarz
5. Barry Venison
6. Liverpool
7. Gordon Chisholm
8. Bob Stokoe
9. Terry Butcher
10. Kevin Phillips
11. Tony Towers
12. Thomas Sorensen
13. Charlie Hurley
14. Dennis Tueart
15. Ally McCoist

MATCH 4   Round 3

Player A
1. Bob Paisley
2. Jimmy Greenhoff
3. Lawrie McMenemy
4. Billy Bremner
5. Charlie George
6. Malcolm MacDonald
7. 1979
8. George Burley
9. Crystal Palace
10. Alan Mullery
11. Everton
12. Dave Watson
13. Stoke City
14. Wimbledon
15. Leicester City

Player B
1. Liverpool
2. Ipswich Town
3. Gianluca Vialli
4. Norman Whiteside

5. Ron Atkinson
6. 1984
7. Geoff Hurst
8. Viv Anderson
9. Tranmere Rovers
10. Fabrizio Ravanelli
11. Martin Chivers
12. Sunderland
13. Andrei Kanchelskis
14. Hillsbrough
15. Oxford United

MATCH 4   Round 4

Player A
1. Paul Scholes
2. Jimmy Rimmer
3. Eight
4. Brian Clough
5. AC Milan
6. Bayern Munich
7. Germany
8. Kevin Keegan
9. Alan Smith
10. Phil Neal
11. Chelsea
12. Terry Venables
13. Leeds United
14. Eintracht Frankfurt
15. Martin Keown

Player B
1. Hungary
2. Real Madrid
3. Rivaldo
4. Alex Ferguson
5. Wim Jansen
6. Super Cup
7. Atletico Madrid
8. Red Star Belgrade
9. Ronald Koeman
10. Rangers
11. Stan Bowles
12. East Germany
13. Francisco Gento
14. Naples
15. Zbigniew Boniek

MATCH 4   Round 5

Player A
1. Bryan Robson
2. Wes Brown
3. Paul Scholes
4. David Platt
5. Arsenal
6. Gary Stevens
7. Roger Hunt
8. Bobby Charlton
9. Italy
10. Stuart Pearce
11. Gianfranco Zola
12. Paul Ince
13. Alan Mullery
14. Luxembourg
15. Bobby Robson

Player B
1. Jack Charlton
2. Ray Houghton
3. Robbie Keane
4. Tony Cascarino
5. Turkey
6. Liam Brady
7. John Aldridge
8. Jason McAteer
9. Kevin Moran
10. Alan McLoughlin
11. Aston Villa
12. John Giles
13. Don Givens
14. Roy Keane
15. Holland

MATCH 4   Round 6

Player A
1. Arsene Wenger
2. Denis Wise
3. Ray Clemence
4. Aston Villa
5. Clive Allen
6. Kevin Ratcliffe
7. Terry McDermott
8. Burnley
9. Bobby Mimms

10. Stuart Pearce
11. First side to win on penalties
12. Davies
13. Mark Bright
14. Stanley Matthews
15. Maidstone

Player B
1. Peter Schmeichel
2. Steve McManaman
3. Wimbledon
4. Chesterfield
5. Attilio Lombardo
6. Leeds United
7. Nottingham Forest
8. Southampton
9. Chris Makin
10. Lawrie Sanchez
11. Goldstone Ground
12. Sergei Rebrov
13. Sepp Maier
14. John Robertson
15. Ron Saunders

MATCH 4
The Group Phase

Player A
1. Turkey
   Poland
   Spain
   Malaysia
2. Ipswich Town
   Manchester City
   Charlton
3. Stanley Matthews
   Bobby Charlton
   Denis Law
   George Best
   Kevin Keegan

Penalty Shoot-out
1. Dennis Bergkamp
2. John Fashanu
3. Palmeiras
4. Martin Peters
5. Stan Cullis

Player B
1. East Stirling
   St. Mirren
   Aberdeen
   Manchester United
2. Juninho
   Nicolas Anelka
   Jimmy Floyd Hasselbaink
3. Aston Villa
   Blackburn Rovers
   Manchester United
   Newcastle United
   Arsenal

Penalty Shoot-out
1. David O'Leary
2. Villa Park
3. Don Revie
4. Roma
5. Dundee United

MATCH 5   Round 1

Player A
1. South African
2. Michael Owen
3. Dean Holdsworth
4. Craig Bellamy
5. Leicester City
6. Alex Ferguson
7. Kevin Keegan
8. Mark Draper
9. Ipswich Town
10. Bob Taylor
11. John Chiedozie
12. Wimbledon
13. Spurs
14. Jamie Cureton
15. Hartlepool

Player B
1. Dundee
2. John Hartson
3. Walsall
4. Robbie Fowler
5. Dave Sexton
6. Reading
7. Wimbledon
8. John Beck
9. Hibernian
10. Swansea/Crewe
11. Sunderland
12. Leeds United
13. Dundee
14. John Burridge
15. Swindon Town

MATCH 5   Round 2

Player A
1. John Barnes
2. Mark Viduka
3. Neil Lennon
4. Kenny Dalglish
5. John Collins
6. Liam Brady
7. Paddy Bonner
8. Mick McCarthy
9. Pierre van Hooijdonk

10. Liverpool
11. Danny McGrain
12. Jimmy McGrory
13. Paolo di Canio
14. Roy Aitken
15. Ronnie Simpson

Player B
1. Ally McCoist
2. Dick Advocaat
3. Graeme Souness
4. Andy Goram
5. Rod Wallace
6. Andrei Kanchelskis
7. Trevor Steven
8. Aberdeen
9. Marco Negri
10. Brian Laudrup
11. Alfie Conn
12. Mark Walters
13. John Greig
14. Raith Rovers
15. Trevor Francis

MATCH 5   Round 3

Player A
1. Manchester United
2. Eric Cantona
3. 1991
4. Chesterfield
5. John Harkes
6. Stevenage
7. Mark Hughes
8. Spurs
9. Malcolm Crosby
10. Southampton
11. Crystal Palace
12. Alan Shearer
13. Brian Moore
14. Joe Royle
15. Stan Collymore

Player B
1. Celtic
2. Hearts
3. Andrei Kanchelskis
4. Pierre van Hooijdonk

259

5. Mark Hateley
6. Craig Burley
7. Charlie Nicholas
8. Dundee United
9. Alex Ferguson
10. Kenny Dalglish
11. Jim Leighton
12. Ally McCoist
13. Hibernian
14. Raith Rovers
15. Richard Gough

MATCH 5 Round 4

Player A
1. Mark Hughes
2. John Hartson
3. Dennis Berkgamp
4. Gianfranco Zola
5. Parma
6. West Ham United
7. Denis Irwin
8. Emmanuel Petit
9. Trevor Steven
10. Alex Ferguson
11. Dinamo Kiev
12. Norman Hunter
13. Real Mallorca
14. Gustavo Poyet
15. Neil Young

Player B
1. Leeds United
2. Ray Parlour
3. Fairs Cup
4. Leeds United
5. Bobby Robson
6. Peter Schmeichel
7. Roy Hodgson
8. France
9. Ray Kennedy
10. Nottingham Forest
11. Wim Jonk
12. QPR
13. Bordeaux
14. Kevin Keegan
15. Coventry City

MATCH 5 Round 5

Player A
1. Germany
2. Diego Maradona
3. Ray Wilkins
4. Archie Gemmell
5. Roberto Baggio
6. Hristo Stoichkov
7. David O'Leary
8. Paul Breitner
9. Robbie Earle
10. Roy Hodgson
11. 1958
12. Dunga
13. Switzerland
14. Van der Kerkhof
15. Paraguay

Player B
1. Brazil
2. Cesar Luis Menotti
3. Rene Higuita
4. Alexei Lalas
5. Jorge Campos
6. 1950
7. Bolivia
8. Roberto Rivelino
9. Daniel Passarella
10. Hugo Sanchez
11. Colombia
12. Diego Simeone
13. Careca
14. Ecuador
15. Costa Rica

MATCH 5 Round 6

Player A
1. Bobby Charlton
2. Graeme Souness
3. Paul Ince
4. Paul Bracewell
5. Portugal
6. West Brom
7. George Camsell
8. Stan Collymore
9. Paul Scholes

10. West Ham
11. Neville Southall
12. Sunderland
13. Home plastic pitch was illegal
14. Bobby Moore
15. Sergei Baltacha

Player B
1. Gary McAllister
2. Vladimir Smicer
3. Pele
4. Nigel Martyn
5. Republic of Ireland
6. Wilf Rostron
7. Gerd Muller
8. Barcelona
9. Uruguay
10. David Neary
11. Mark Lawrenson
12. Brian Clough
13. Sutton United
14. Sepp Blatter
15. Roy Essandoh

MATCH 5
The Group Phase

Player A
1. Brazil
   Germany
   Argentina
2. Ipswich Town
   Wolves
   Newcastle United
   Manchester City
   Aston Villa
   Everton
3. Arsenal
   Nottingham Forest
   Everton

Penalty Shoot-out
1. Oxford United
2. Eric Cantona
3. David Platt
4. Peter Shreeves
5. Atletico Madrid

Player B
1. Don Givens
   Frank Stapleton
   John Aldridge
   Niall Quinn
   Tony Cascarino
2. Celtic
   Steaua Bucharest
   Hamburg
   Marseilles
3. Ron Atkinson
   Brian Little
   John Gregory

Penalty Shoot-out
1. Roger Milla
2. Ionel Ganea
3. Mark Stein
4. Vinnie Jones
5. Crewe Alexandra

MATCH 6   Round 1

Player A
1. Sander Westerveld
2. Sammy McIlroy
3. Alan Shearer
4. Stuart Pearce
5. Crewe Alexandra
6. Port Vale
7. Plymouth Argyle
8. Watney Cup
9. Northwich Victoria
10. Nottingham Forest
11. Michael Owen
12. Bjarne Goldbaek
13. Crystal Palace
14. Aston Villa
15. Marcus Gayle

Player B
1. Reading
2. Bermuda
3. Teddy Sheringham
4. Stoke City
5. John Hartson
6. Colin Hendry
7. Georgi Kinkladze
8. Alan Rough
9. Q. P. R
10. Swansea
11. Hearts
12. Huddersfield Town
13. All penalties
14. Newcastle United
15. Blackpool

MATCH 6   Round 2

Player A
1. Gianluca Vialli
2. Ed de Goey
3. Jimmy Floyd Hasselbaink
4. Dennis Wise
5. Manchester United
6. Glenn Hoddle
7. Albert Ferrer
8. Brian Laudrup
9. George Weah

10. Gavin Peacock
11. Jimmy Greaves
12. Graham Roberts
13. Watford
14. Ted Drake
15. Chris Sutton

Player B
1. Manchester United
2. Jean Tigana
3. George Cohen
4. Kevin Keegan
5. Wolves
6. John Collins
7. Paul Peschisolido
8. Karl-Heinz Reidle
9. Andy Cole
10. Bobby Robson
11. Louis Saha
12. Geoff Horsfield
13. Johnny Haynes
14. Rodney Marsh
15. Bill Dodgin (snr and jnr)

MATCH 6   Round 3

Player A
1. Trevor Brooking
2. Mark Hughes
3. Newcastle United
4. Kasey Keller
5. Brighton
6. Liverpool
7. Jim Montgomery
8. Alan Hansen
9. Everton
10. Billy Bremner
11. Christopher Wreh
12. Andy Townsend
13. Newcastle United
14. Norwich City
15. Joe Corrigan

Player B
1. Marc Overmars
2. Peter Schmeichel
3. Gary Pallister
4. Daniel Amokachi

5. Wrexham
6. Mark Hughes
7. Gary Charles
8. Kenny Dalglish
9. Roy Keane
10. Mark Bright
11. Ronnie Rosenthal
12. Stuart Pearce
13. Cambridge United
14. John Barnes
15. Glenn Hoddle

MATCH 6   Round 4

Player A
1. Liverpool
2. Dundee United
3. West Germany
4. Galatasaray
5. Keith Burkenshaw
6. Newcastle United
7. Paul Ince
8. Jurgen Klinsmann
9. Aston Villa
10. Borussia Dortmund
11. Wolves
12. John Wark
13. Valencia
14. Leeds United
15. Ronaldo

Player B
1. Yugoslavia
2. Ruud van Nistlerooy
3. Anderlecht
4. Roberto Baggio
5. Real Madrid
6. Johan Cruyff
7. Hakan Sukur
8. Claudio Ranieri
9. Benfica
10. Roma
11. Stephane Guivarc'h
12. Hungarian
13. Giovanni Trapattoni
14. Kaiserslauten
15. Cologne

MATCH 6   Round 5

Player A
1. Frank Lampard (junior)
2. Italy
3. David Rocastle
4. Leeds United
5. Bryan Robson
6. Paul Scholes
7. 1993
8. Taylor (Graham and Peter)
9. Luton Town
10. Chris Sutton
11. France
12. Uruguay
13. Terry Butcher
14. 48
15. Marcelo Salas

Player B
1. Ian Rush
2. Billy Bingham
3. Gary McAllister
4. Dean Saunders
5. Sammy McIlroy
6. Scott Gemmell
7. Vinnie Jones
8. George Best
9. Matt Elliott
10. John Toshack
11. David Healy
12. Costa Rica
13. Pat van den Hauwe
14. Norman Whiteside
15. Joe Jordan

MATCH 6   Round 6

Player A
1. Jamie Redknapp
2. Sunderland
3. Chris Powell
4. Peter Beardsley
5. Billy McNeill
6. Alan and Gary Kelly
7. Marseille
8. Notts County
9. Lincoln City

10. Andy Gray
11. Romania
12. Switzerland
13. Leeds United
14. Atletico Madrid
15. Coventry City

Player B
1. Highfield Road
2. Marseille
3. Aberdeen
4. Germany
5. Dave Bassett
6. Dennis Wise
7. Alan Smith
8. Dwight Yorke
9. Les Ferdinand
10. David Thompson
11. Jock Stein
12. Clive and Paul Allen
13. Stockport County
14. Ian St John
15. Alex Dawson

MATCH 6
The Group Phase

Player A
1. Leicester City
   Stoke City
   Nottingham Forest
   Southampton
   Derby County
2. Manchester City
   Spurs
   Aston Villa
   Nottingham Forest
3. Manchester United
   Liverpool
   Sunderland

Penalty Shoot-out
1. Tom Finney
2. Mario Zagalo
3. Alan Shearer
4. Terry Venables
5. Everton

Player B
1. Phil Parkes
   Ray Clemence
   Gary Bailey
   Dave Beasant
   David Seaman
2. AC Milan
   Manchester United
   Ajax
   Liverpool
   Barcelona
3. Bryan and Bobby Robson
   Jim and Walter Smith

Penalty Shoot-out
1. Arsenal
2. Mick Mills
3. Dave Bassett
4. Micky Thomas
5. Bobby Johnstone

MATCH 7   Round 1

Player A
1. Andrei Kanchelskis
2. Tottenham Hotspur
3. Mark Bosnich
4. Cambridge Utd
5. Ricky Villa
6. Peter Beardsley
7. Dan Petrescu
8. Ron Atkinson
9. Lee Bowyer
10. Q. P. R
11. Cambridge United
12. Sheffield Wednesday
13. Manchester United
14. Patrick Kluivert
15. Marc Overmars

Player B
1. Gerry Francis
2. Dennis Bergkamp
3. Faustino Asprilla
4. Tony Adams
5. Carlisle United
6. Stanley Matthews
7. Steve Bruce
8. Jock Stein
9. Dave Challinor
10. Andy Sinton
11. Preston
12. George Best
13. Lee Dixon
14. Lee Sharpe
15. Portsmouth

MATCH 7   Round 2

Player A
1. Martin Peters
2. Jermaine Defoe
3. Manchester United
4. Tony Cottee
5. Arsenal
6. Joe Cole
7. Stan Lazaridis
8. Ian Wright
9. Trevor Brooking

10. Ron Greenwood
11. Geoff Hurst
12. Bolton Wanderers
13. Alan Sealey
14. Bryan 'Pop' Robson
15. Ray Stewart

Player B
1. Alan Curbishley
2. Shaun Bartlett
3. Glasgow Rangers
4. Andy Hunt
5. Selhurst Park/Upton Park
6. The Addicks
7. Robert Lee
8. Mike Bailey
9. Clive Mendonca
10. Blackburn Rovers
11. South Africa
12. Alan Mullery
13. Huddersfield Town
14. Sam Bartram
15. Derby or Burnley

MATCH 7   Round 3

Player A
1. Emile Heskey
2. Ian Rush
3. Nottingham Forest
4. Dean Saunders
5. Denis Irwin
6. Jeff Astle
7. Justin Edinburgh
8. Savo Milosevic
9. Wimbledon
10. Alan Thompson
11. Stein (Brian and Mark)
12. Old Trafford
13. Roy Keane
14. Asa Hartford
15. Kenny Dalglish

Player B
1. Ray Clemence
2. Eric Cantona
3. Emerson
4. Brian Kilcline

5. Alan Shearer
6. Mark Crossley
7. Pat Rice
8. West Ham United
9. Sunderland
10. Pat van den Hauwe
11. Bill Shankly
12. Mick Jones
13. Ian Callaghan
14. All scored by different players
15. Telford United

MATCH 7   Round 4

Player A
1. Lee Bowyer
2. Aston Villa
3. Chelsea
4. Blackburn Rovers
5. Franz Thijssen
6. Manchester City
7. Aberdeen
8. John Hollins
9. Ally McCoist
10. Plastic pitch illegal
11. Leeds United
12. Lens
13. Francois van der Elst
14. Kevin Sheedy
15. Spurs

Player B
1. Bob Paisley
2. Barcelona
3. Kanu
4. Tony Barton
5. Trevor Francis
6. Luis van Gaal
7. Benfica
8. Gerd Muller
9. Real Madrid
10. Rome
11. Franco Baresi
12. Besiktas
13. Bayern Munich
14. Derby County
15. Laurie Cunningham

MATCH 7   Round 5

Player A
1. Zinedine Zidane
2. Roberto Baggio
3. Cameroon
4. Croatia
5. Turin
6. Roger Milla
7. Sweden
8. Jose Luis Chilavert
9. Mark Wright
10. Lothar Matthaus
11. John Aldridge
12. Robert Prosinecki
13. Peter Shilton
14. Sweden
15. Italy

Player B
1. Paolo Rossi
2. Harald Schumacher
3. Portugal
4. Norman Whiteside
5. Pat Jennings
6. Diego Maradona
7. Algeria
8. Emilio Butragueno
9. Belgium
10. Hungary
11. Spain
12. Mal Donaghy
13. Karl Heinz Rummenigge
14. France
15. Igor Belanov

MATCH 7   Round 6

Player A
1. Australian
2. Martin O'Neill
3. Lazio
4. Maracana Stadium (Brazil)
5. Gerry Francis
6. Aberdeen
7. Neville Southall
8. Gordon Taylor

9. Daniel Amokachi
10. Franco Baresi
11. Kevin Richardson
12. Gordon Banks
13. Nicky Butt
14. Abandoned due to lights
    failure
15. Wim Jansen

Player B
1. Ken Bates
2. Barry Fry
3. John Aldridge
4. Benfica
5. Nayim
6. Middlesbrough
7. Diego Simeone
8. Gary Neville
9. Poland
10. Marco Negri
11. Benfica
12. Hull City
13. Nat Lofthouse
14. Russell Lapaty
15. Reading

MATCH 7
The Group Phase

Player A
1. Roberto Baggio
    Gabriel Batistuta
    Guiseppe Signori
2. Tommy Gemmell
    Steve Chalmers
    Kenny Dalglish
    John Robertson
3. Arsenal
    Fulham
    Bristol City
    Newcastle United
    Manchester United

Penalty Shoot-out
1. Port Vale
2. Jimmy Greaves
3. Rotherham United
4. Argentina

5. Brisbane (Road)

Player B
The Group Phase
1. Manchester City
    Oldham Athletic
    Swindon Town
2. Ian Wright
    Eric Cantona
    Mark Hughes
    Roberto di Matteo
3. Arbroath
    Alloa
    Airdrieonians
    Albion Rovers
    Ayr United

Penalty Shoot-out
1. Nottingham Forest
2. Wealdstone
3. Lee Dixon
4. Alfredo di Stefano
5. QPR

MATCH 8   Round 1

Player A
1. Manchester United
2. Jimmy-Floyd Hasselbaink
3. Graham Taylor
4. Ian Rush
5. Newcastle United
6. Sheffield United
7. Tim Flowers
8. Lee Sharpe
9. West Ham United
10. York City
11. Woking
12. Nico Claesen
13. Peter Withe
14. Brendon Batson
15. Crystal Palace

Player B
1. WBA
2. Arsenal
3. Three
4. Steve Watson
5. Larry Lloyd
6. John Aldridge
7. Peter Beardsley
8. Spurs
9. Robbie Keane
10. Wimbledon
11. Graham Stuart
12. Aston Villa
13. Leicester city
14. Robbie Fowler
15. Scarborough

MATCH 8   Round 2

Player A
1. Stuart Pearce
2. Pierre Van Hooijdonk
3. Dave Beasant
4. Liverpool
5. Peter Taylor
6. Ron Atkinson
7. Kenny Burns
8. Garry Birtles
9. Sheffield Wednesday
10. Andrea Silenzia
11. Frank Clark
12. Bob McKinlay
13. Lee Chapman
14. Blackburn Rovers
15. John O'Hare

Player B
1. Baseball Ground
2. Jim Smith
3. Republic of Ireland
4. Jamaica
5. Christian Dailly
6. Colin Todd
7. Paolo Wanchope
8. Seth Johnson
9. Dave Mackay
10. Roy McFarland
11. Finn Harps
12. Peter Shilton
13. John Gregory
14. Kevin Hector
15. Colin Boulton

MATCH 8   Round 3

Player A
1. Matt Elliott
2. Bryan Robson
3. Bolton Wanderers
4. John Lukic
5. Nigel Clough
6. Maine Road
7. Ian Rush
8. Everton
9. Ron Saunders
10. West Ham
11. 1967
12. George Graham
13. Nigel Winterburn
14. Alan Kennedy
15. Denis Tueart

Player B
1. Arsenal
2. Sunderland
3. Old Trafford
4. Hereford United

5. Bertie Mee
6. Brian Talbot
7. Lawrie McMenemy
8. Bobby Moore
9. Kevin Keegan
10. Martin Buchan
11. John Giles
12. Dave Sexton
13. Alan Taylor
14. Bobby Kerr
15. John Motson

MATCH 8   Round 4

Player A
1. Santos
2. Uruguay
3. Copa Libertadores
4. Chile
5. Brazil
6. Palmeiras
7. Independiente
8. Maracana
9. Romario
10. Paraguay
11. Huracan
12. Colombia
13. Boca Juniors
14. He was a goalkeeper (Jose Luis Chilavert)
15. Racing Club

Player B
1. David Platt
2. Sven Goran Eriksson
3. Italy
4. Bayern Munich
5. Real Madrid
6. Barcelona
7. Ian Rush
8. Roberto Baggio
9. Feyenoord
10. Bruges
11. Sepp Maier
12. Castilla
13. Juventus
14. Oleg Blochin
15. Rheims

MATCH 8   Round 5

Player A
1. David Beckham
2. Germany
3. Brazil
4. Luther Blissett
5. David Platt
6. Gary Pallister
7. Kenny Sansom
8. Cameroon
9. Dave Watson
10. Seth Johnson
11. Peter Davenport
12. Republic of Ireland
13. David James
14. Paul Mariner
15. Austria

Player B
1. Mark Hughes
2. Ian Dowie
3. Jock Stein
4. Millenium Stadium
5. Martin O'Neill
6. Denis Law
7. Kevin Ratcliffe
8. George Best
9. Alan McInally
10. Holland
11. Bryan Hamilton
12. Estonia
13. Dean Saunders
14. Norman Whiteside
15. Tom Boyd

MATCH 8   Round 6

Player A
1. Norman Whiteside
2. Michel Platini
3. Aston Villa
4. Nicolas Anelka
5. Man City
6. Denis Irwin
7. Chris Sutton
8. Ajax
9. Laurie Cunningham

10. Ferenc Puskas
11. AC Milan
12. Glasgow
13. Lincoln City
14. Mark Hughes
15. Bruce Rioch

Player B
1. Paul Jones
2. Dietmar Hamann
3. Everton
4. Leicester City
5. Fulham
6. Jean Marc Bosman
7. Ron Moran
8. Lazio
9. Everton
10. Italy
11. Notts County
12. Alan Oakes
13. Chester City
14. Peter Barnes
15. Ted McDougall

MATCH 8
The Group Phase

Player A
1. Alan Shearer
   Andy Cole
   Kevin Phillips
2. Gerd Muller
   Rudi Voller
   Uwe Seeler
   Jurgen Klinsmann
   Karl-Heinz Rummenigge
3. Everton
   Liverpool
   Manchester United
   Arsenal

Penalty Shoot-out
1. Nigel Winterburn
2. Mal Donaghy
3. Belgium
4. Joe Royle
5. Tony Cottee

Player B
1. Bayern Munich
   Hamburg
   Bayer Leverkusen
2. Trevor Francis
   Ray Wilkins
   Glenn Hoddle
   Gordon Strachan
   Bryan Robson
   Peter Reid
   Stuart Pearce
3. David Beckham
   Gary Neville

Penalty Shoot-out
1. Patrick Kluivert
2. Viv Anderson
3. Mike Summerbee
4. John Wark
5. John Hartson

MATCH 9   Round 1

Player A
1. Chelsea
2. Brentford
3. Ryan Giggs
4. Hearts
5. Viv Anderson
6. Chester
7. Manchester United
8. Berwick Rangers
9. Luther Blissett
10. Andy Clarke
11. Jimmy Floyd Hasselbaink
12. Preston
13. Burnley
14. Stoke City
15. Ipswich Town

Player B
1. Michael Knighton
2. Ian Wright
3. Bristol Rovers
4. Savo Milosevic
5. Chelsea
6. Newcastle United
7. Glenn Hoddle
8. Birmingham City
9. Arsenal
10. Ron Atkinson
11. Aston Villa
12. Allen (Clive, Malcolm and Paul)
13. Dave Sexton
14. Kerry Dixon
15. Hartlepool

MATCH 9   Round 2

Player A
1. Karren Brady
2. Trevor Francis
3. Steve Claridge
4. Dele Adebola
5. Port Vale
6. Barry Fry
7. Watford
8. Paul Tait

9. Alberto Tarantini
10. Willie Bell
11. Bob Latchford
12. Tony Coton
13. Leeds United
14. Aston Villa
15. Manchester City

Player B
1. Ugo Ehiogu
2. Dwight Yorke
3. Joszef Vengelos
4. Mark Bosnich
5. Leicester City
6. Leeds United
7. Mark Delaney
8. Bolton Wanderers
9. David Platt
10. Paul McGrath
11. Chris Nicholl
12. Ron Saunders
13. Tony Morley
14. Jimmy Rimmer
15. Gordon Cowans

MATCH 9   Round 3

Player A
1. Liverpool
2. Bob Stokoe
3. Arsenal
4. Roy Evans
5. Chelsea
6. Blackburn Rovers
7. Paul Stewart
8. Clive Walker
9. David Speedie
10. Chris Waddle
11. Eric Cantona
12. Spurs
13. Aston Villa
14. Stoke City
15. Accrington Stanley

Player B
1. Ian Wright
2. Steve Coppell
3. Middlesbrough

271

4. Mark Wright
5. Eric Cantona
6. Stuart Pearce
7. Mark Hughes
8. Wimbledon
9. Luton Town
10. Jim Leighton
11. Ruud Gullit
12. Ian Rush
13. Upton Park
14. Duncan Ferguson
15. John Byrne

MATCH 9   Round 4

Player A
1. Bernabeu
2. Terry Venables
3. Deportivo La Coruna
4. De Boer (Frank and Ronald)
5. Johann Cruyff
6. Alfredo di Stefano
7. Valencia
8. Rivaldo
9. Emilio Butragueno
10. Athletic Bilbao
11. Bernd Schuster
12. Bayern Munich
13. Antonio Zubizerreta
14. Espanol
15. Romario

Player B
1. Lazio
2. Milan
3. Juventus
4. Gabriel Batistuta
5. Napoli
6. AC Milan
7. Paolo Rossi
8. Dino Zoff
9. Hernan Crespo
10. Turin
11. Arrigo Sacchi
12. Inter Milan
13. Michel Platini
14. Torino

15. Parma

MATCH 9   Round 5

Player A
1. Belgium
2. Steve McManaman
3. Savo Milosevic
4. Kevin Keegan
5. Spain
6. Italy
7. Trezeguet
8. Raul
9. Yugoslavia
10. Georghe Hagi
11. Frank Rijkaard
12. Michael Owen
13. Muzzy Izzet
14. Charleroi
15. Sergio Concencaio

Player B
1. Spain
2. Ally McCoist
3. Holland
4. Davor Suker
5. Czech Republic
6. Gary McAllister
7. Patrick Kluivert
8. Ian Walker
9. Croatia
10. Hristo Stoichkov
11. Switzerland
12. Andy Moller
13. Old Trafford
14. Florin Raducioiu
15. Turkey

MATCH 9   Round 6

Player A
1. Graham Taylor
2. Tony Adams
3. Fulham
4. Grampus 8
5. Mark Lawrenson
6. Cyril
7. Don Masson

8. San Marino
9. York City
10. Swindon Town
11. Edgar Davids
12. Peter Bonetti
13. Barnsley
14. Bill Nicholson
15. John Sissons

Player B
1. Michael Ball
2. Watford
3. Barnsley
4. Jurgen Klinsmann
5. Bayern Munich
6. Terry Venables
7. Cobi Jones
8. Ian Wright
9. Pat Jennings
10. Jack Charlton
11. Aston Villa
12. Chesterfield
13. Ruud Gullit
14. Steve McMahon
15. Soviet Union

MATCH 9
The Group Phase

Player A
1. Ajax
   Bayern Munich
   Juventus
   Barcelona
2. Kenny Dalglish
   Terry Venables
   George Graham
   Graeme Souness
   Joe Royle
   Gianluca Vialli
3. Newcastle United
   Exeter

Penalty Shoot-out
1. Joszef Venglos
2. Tore-Andre Flo
3. Gordon Banks
4. Georghe Hagi

5. West Brom

Player B
1. Uruguay
   Germany
   Brazil
   Italy
   Chile
   France
2. Lee Sharpe
   Ryan Giggs
   David Beckham
3. Howard Wilkinson
   Howard Kendall
   Joe Fagan

Penalty Shoot-out
1. Brazil
2. Gordon Strachan
3. Denis Law
4. Bobby Moore
5. McLean (Jim and Tommy)

MATCH 10   Round 1

Player A
1. Bruce Grobbelaar
2. Nicolas Anelka
3. Jimmy Floyd Hasselbaink
4. Kenny Dalglish
5. Dundee
6. Sylvain Wiltord
7. Everton
8. Kilmarnock
9. West Brom
10. Faustino Asprilla
11. David Hopkin
12. Daniel Dichio
13. Willie Fagan
14. Tommy Burns
15. Manchester United

Player B
1. Kenny Dalglish
2. Denis Law
3. Jimmy Greaves
4. Hull City
5. Laurie Cunningham
6. Blackburn Rovers
7. Aston Villa
8. Alan Sunderland
9. Gordon McQueen
10. Frank Lampard
11. John Scales
12. Danny Wallace
13. Newcastle United
14. Aston Villa
15. Tony Book

MATCH 10   Round 2

Player A
1. Kenny Dalglish
2. Jack Walker
3. Colin Hendry
4. Tim Flowers
5. Mike Newell
6. Simon Garner
7. Tim Sherwood
8. Jason Wilcox
9. Derek Fazackerley
10. Tim Flowers
11. Nathan Blake
12. Kevin Davies
13. Norwich City
14. Ron Clayton
15. Lee Carsley

Player B
1. Burnden Park
2. Eidur Gudjohnsen
3. South African
4. Jason McAteer
5. Tranmere Rovers
6. John McGinlay
7. Phil Neal
8. Manchester United
9. Frank Worthington
10. Nat Lofthouse
11. Peter Reid
12. Andy Walker
13. Stanley Mortensen
14. Eddie Hopkinson
15. Ian Greaves

MATCH 10   Round 3

Player A
1. West Ham
2. Joe Royle
3. Wimbledon
4. Ian Wright
5. Peter Shilton
6. Bryan Robson
7. Zenith Data Systems
8. Bobby Charlton
9. Earl Barrett
10. Brian Clough
11. Burnley
12. Milk Marketing Board
13. Clint Hill
14. Spurs
15. Geoff Hurst

Player B
1. Everton
2. Kenny Dalglish
3. John Aldridge
4. Spurs

5. Jesper Olsen
6. John Aldridge
7. Arsenal
8. Leeds United
9. Dave Bennett
10. Glenn Hoddle
11. Watford
12. John Lyall
13. Liverpool
14. Peter Willis
15. Paul Power

MATCH 10   Round 4

Player A
1. Nou Camp
2. Gianluca Vialli
3. Lev Yashin
4. Ruud Gullit
5. Aberdeen
6. AC Milan
7. Anderlecht
8. Paris St Germain
9. Cologne
10. Gothenburg
11. Barcelona
12. Pedraig Mijatovic
13. San Siro
14. Karl Heinz Reidle
15. Budapest

Player B
1. Kevin Keegan
2. Dennis Wise
3. Newcastle United
4. Bruce Grobbelaar
5. Brian Laudrup
6. Chelsea
7. Watford
8. West Ham United
9. Tony Parks
10. Robert Lee
11. Ian Bowyer
12. Graham Rix
13. Dynamo Moscow
14. Burnley
15. John Hewitt

MATCH 10   Round 5

Player A
1. Marco van Basten
2. John Jensen
3. Jean Tigana
4. Russia
5. Gerd Muller
6. Michel Platini
7. Italy
8. Spain
9. Arnold Muhren
10. Holland
11. Portugal
12. Malta
13. Uli Hoeness
14. John Sivebaek
15. Horst Hrubesch

Player B
1. Paul Scholes
2. Dan Petrescu
3. Brazil
4. Dennis Wise
5. Marco van Basten
6. Tony Adams
7. Steve Bull
8. David Platt
9. Michael Gray
10. Mike Channon
11. Sampdoria
12. David Beckham
13. Uruguay
14. Alan Mullery
15. China

MATCH 10   Round 6

Player A
1. Nick Barmby
2. 1994
3. Fulham
4. Ruud Gullit
5. West Brom
6. Christian Gross
7. Italy
8. Mark Hateley
9. Porto

10. Oxford United
11. Wolves
12. Jan Tomaszewski
13. Gary McAllister
14. Bristol
15. England

Player B
1. Manchester United
2. George Best
3. Pele
4. Bobby Gould
5. Aberdeen
6. Leicester City
7. Luton Town
8. Les Ferdinand
9. Nigel Spackman
10. Swansea City
11. Jim Beglin
12. Scotland
13. Robbie Fowler
14. Steffen Iversen
15. David Connelly

MATCH 10
The Group Phase

Player A
1. Ray Harford
   Roy Hodgson
   Brian Kidd
   Tony Parkes
   Graeme Souness
2. Bayern Munich
   Galatasaray
3. Luton Town
   Southampton
   Crystal Palace
   West Ham United
   Queens Park Rangers

Penalty Shoot-out
1. Didier Deschamps
2. Trevor Brooking
3. Bradford City
4. Eric Cantona
5. West Brom

Player B
1. Paul Scholes
   Teddy Sheringham
   Paul Rideout
   Eddie Newton
2. Zaire
   Holland
   New Zealand
   Sweden
3. John McGovern
   Colin Todd
   Bruce Rioch
   Roy McFarland

Penalty Shoot-out
1. Harry Kewell
2. Walter Smith
3. Mexico
4. Finland
5. Germany

MATCH 11   Round 1

Player A
1. Aston Villa
2. Coventry City
3. Darren Anderton
4. Wimbledon
5. Arthur Albiston
6. Stoke
7. Wigan Athletic
8. Peterborough
9. Steve Perryman
10. Preston North End
11. Spurs
12. QPR
13. Nottingham Forest
14. Des Walker
15. Bolton Wanderers

Player B
1. Plymouth Argyle
2. Middlesbrough
3. Steve Coppell
4. Tony Adams
5. Aston Villa
6. Stan Collymore
7. Derby County
8. Shrewsbury
9. Nottingham Forest
10. Rodney Marsh
11. He was sacked
12. Gillingham
13. John Byrne
14. Micky Adams
15. Cambridge United

MATCH 11   Round 2

Player A
1. Delia Smith
2. Steve Bruce
3. Chris Sutton
4. Bryan Hamilton
5. Sunderland
6. Iwan Roberts
7. Mike Walker
8. Inter Milan
9. Efan Ekoku
10. Andy Linighan
11. Mark Robins
12. Sutton United
13. Rochdale
14. Mark Bowen
15. Spurs

Player B
1. Kieron Dyer
2. David Johnson
3. Richard Wright
4. Craig Forrest
5. Sir Alf Ramsey
6. Marcus Stewart
7. Jason Dozzell
8. Roger Osborne
9. Alan Brazil
10. David Johnson
11. Johnny Metgod
12. Frans Thijssen
13. John Lyall
14. Fulham
15. Ray Crawford

MATCH 11   Round 3

Player A
1. Arsenal
2. Dagenham & Redbridge
3. Ron Atkinson
4. Gustavo Poyet
5. Sunderland
6. Terry Venables
7. Ron Radford
8. David O'Leary
9. Oldham Athletic
10. Manchester City
11. Gary Mabbutt
12. Greenhoff
13. Gary Ablett
14. Chelsea
15. Nottingham Forest (Brian and Nigel Clough)

Player B
1. Ipswich Town
2. Kenny Dalglish
3. Sunderland

4. Clive Mendonca
5. Manchester City
6. Sunderland
7. Martin O'Neill
8. Bolton
9. Steve Claridge
10. Chris Kamara
11. Glenn Hoddle
12. Charlton Athletic
13. Steve Walsh
14. Notts County
15. Chelsea

MATCH 11 Round 4

Player A
1. Andy Cole
2. Ray Clemence
3. Ian Wright
4. Billy McNeill
5. Barcelona
6. Gary Lineker
7. Alan Smith
8. Sheffield Wednesday
9. John Toshack
10. Swansea City
11. Old Trafford
12. Ray Crawford
13. Juventus
14. Trevor Whymark
15. Manchester City

Player B
1. John Robertson
2. Benfica
3. Emlyn Hughes
4. Jari Litmanen
5. Holland
6. Leeds United 1975
7. Bayern Munich
8. Jock Stein
9. Barcelona
10. CSKA Sofia
11. Fiorentina
12. Gray (Eddie and Frank)
13. Celtic
14. Patrick Kluivert
15. Barcelona

MATCH 11 Round 5

Player A
1. Gary Lineker
2. Cameroon
3. Lawrie McMenemy
4. Italy
5. Wales
6. Glenn Hoddle
7. Emile Heskey
8. David White
9. Elland Road
10. Norman Hunter
11. Bryan Robson
12. Hungary
13. France
14. Duncan Edwards
15. Emlyn Hughes

Player B
1. Craig Brown
2. Kenny Dalglish
3. Don Hutchison
4. Neil Sullivan
5. Ally McCoist
6. Denis Law
7. Richard Gough
8. Craig Burley
9. Paul Lambert
10. Brazil
11. Australia
12. Willie Ormond
13. Joe Jordan
14. CIS
15. Hansen

MATCH 11 Round 6

Player A
1. Dixie Dean
2. Michael Bridges
3. Edgar Davids
4. Leeds United
5. Paul Ince
6. Halifax Town
7. Huddersfield
8. Paul Allen
9. Michel Platini

278

10. Ferenc Puskas
11. Reg Matthews
12. Roma
13. Aston Villa
14. Alan Mullery
15. Dundee United

Player B
1. Grimsby Town
2. Bradford City
3. Alan Hansen
4. Paul Jewell
5. Howard Kendall
6. Massimo Taibi
7. Southampton
8. Barcelona
9. Mark Wallington
10. John Charles
11. Pat Jennings
12. Andy Thorne
13. Perry Suckling
14. Willie Johnstone
15. West Brom

MATCH 11
The Group Phase

Player A
1. Halifax
   Hartlepool
   Huddersfield
   Hull City
2. Brian Clough
   George Graham
   Bob Paisley
3. Sunderland
   Manchester City
   Stoke City
   Southampton
   Werder Bremen

Penalty Shoot-out
1. Barnsley
2. West Ham
3. Steve McManaman
4. Lothar Matthaus
5. Morocco

Player B
1. Dimitri Kharine
   Freud Grodas
   Ed de Goey
2. Alan Shearer
   Les Ferdinand
   Ian Wright
   Robbie Fowler
   Andy Cole
   Matt Le Tissier
3. John Salako
   Ian Wright
   Geoff Thomas

Penalty Shoot-out
1. Robert Maxwell
2. Alan Shearer
3. Esteban Fuentes
4. Wendy Toms
5. Calais

MATCH 12   Round 1

Player A
1. Liverpool
2. Arsenal
3. John Hartson
4. Hartlepool
5. Ron Atkinson
6. Manchester City
7. Villa Park
8. Dean Holdsworth
9. Scunthorpe United
10. Brian Flynn
11. Halifax Town
12. He scored twice for each side
13. Plymouth Argyle
14. Hereford United
15. George Eastham

Player B
1. George Graham
2. Denis Irwin
3. Alex Ferguson
4. Chelsea
5. Roy Evans
6. Neville Southall
7. Liverpool
8. Megson (Don and Gary)
9. Notts County
10. Chelsea
11. Dave Mackay
12. Dick Advocaat
13. Ron Saunders
14. Wycombe Wanderers
15. Charlton (Bobby and Jack)

MATCH 12   Round 2

Player A
1. Robbie Keane
2. Darren Huckerby
3. Magnus Hedman
4. Dion Dublin
5. Steve Ogrizovic
6. Ron Atkinson
7. Jimmy Hill
8. John Aloisi
9. Viorel Moldovan
10. Phil Babb
11. Eion Jess
12. Peter Ndluvo
13. Mick Quinn
14. Terry Butcher
15. Bobby Gould

Player B
1. Tony Cottee
2. Gerry Taggart
3. Gordon Banks
4. Peter Shilton
5. Steve Guppy
6. Crewe
7. Manchester City
8. Mark McGhee
9. Peggy Arphexad
10. Gary Lineker
11. David Nish
12. Stan Collymore
13. Atletico Madrid
14. Graham Cross
15. John O'Neill

MATCH 12   Round 3

Player A
1. Inverness Caledonian Thistle
2. Walter Smith
3. Chris Woods
4. Aberdeen
5. Dundee
6. Wallace
7. Mark Walters
8. Kilmarnock
9. Paul Gascoigne
10. Celtic
11. Gordon Strachan
12. Aberdeen
13. Gordon Durie
14. Only final won by penalties
15. Airdrie

Player B

1. Littlewoods
2. Gianluca Vialli
3. Newcastle United
4. Brian Clough
5. Roberto di Matteo
6. Tony Adams
7. Portsmouth
8. Dennis Bergkamp
9. Woking
10. Clayton Blackmore
11. Liverpool
12. West Ham
13. Roy Keane
14. Sheffield United
15. Aston Villa

MATCH 12   Round 4

Player A

1. Ajax
2. Slovakia
3. Franz Beckenbauer
4. Howard Kendall
5. Karl Heinz Rummenigge
6. Moscow
7. Gianluca Vialli
8. Tony Yeboah
9. Porto
10. Sampdoria
11. Monaco
12. Paolo di Canio
13. AZ Alkmaar
14. Paris St Germain
15. Andrei Shevchenko

Player B

1. Tore Andre Flo
2. Roberto Carlos
3. Attilio Lombardo
4. Alessandro del Piero
5. Raul
6. John Collins
7. Dwight Yorke
8. Marcel Desailly
9. Malmo
10. Paris
11. Ajax

12. de Boer (Ronald and Frank)
13. Phil Neal
14. Benfica
15. Graeme Le Saux

MATCH 12   Round 5

Player A

1. Brazil
2. Iran
3. Emmanuel Petit
4. Andreas Brehme
5. North Korea
6. Uruguay
7. Mario Zagalo
8. Hungary
9. Cameroon
10. Paolo Rossi
11. Felix
12. Czechoslovakia
13. Berti Vogts
14. Goodison Park
15. 1998

Player B

1. Sir Alf Ramsey
2. Bobby Moore
3. David Platt
4. Lee Sharpe
5. Alvin Martin
6. Morocco
7. Martin Keown
8. Charltons
9. Paul Scholes
10. Gareth Southgate
11. Brian Deane
12. Kevin Keegan
13. Warren Barton
14. Trevor Cherry
15. Tony Woodcock

MATCH 12   Round 6

Player A

1. Gordon Banks
2. Paul Gascoigne
3. Thierry Henry

4. Hungary
5. Mark Viduka
6. Chelsea
7. Bayern Munich
8. Dave Beasant
9. Tony Brown
10. Spurs
11. Tony Cottee
12. France
13. Real Sociedad
14. Jackie Milburn
15. Little (Alan and Brian)

Player B
1. Inter Milan
2. Robbie Fowler
3. Stanley Matthews
4. Wilkins
5. Swansea City
6. Dominic Matteo
7. Yugoslavia
8. Morocco
9. Meadowbank Thistle
10. Graeme Le Saux
11. Neville
12. Kenny Dalglish
13. Juventus
14. Sweden
15. Japan

MATCH 12
The Group Phase

Player A
1. West Ham
   Liverpool
2. Stan Collymore
   Carlton Palmer
   Nick Barmby
   Mark Hughes
   Dean Saunders
   John Hartson
   Don Hutchison
   Dan Petrescu
3. Graeme Souness
   Trevor Francis

Penalty Shoot-out
1. Dennis Bergkamp
2. Alan Ball
3. Bulgaria
4. Barry Hayles
5. Fighting each other

Player B
1. Peter Beardsley
   David Batty
   Gordon Cowans
2. Gary Lineker
   Jimmy Greaves
3. John Gregory
   Alan Curbishley
   Gordon Strachan
   George Burley
   David O'Leary
   Joe Royle
   Harry Redknapp

Penalty Shoot-out
1. France
2. Frank Stapleton
3. Keith Burkenshaw
4. Billy Wright
5. Mark Bosnich

Player A
1. Australian
2. Steve McLaren
3. Joe Kinnear
4. Barnsley
5. Darren Purse
6. Andy Ritchie
7. Bobby Robson
8. Graham Taylor
9. Mike Trebilcock
10. Torquay
11. Brad Friedel
12. Vladimir Kinder
13. Nottingham Forest
14. Bryan Robson
15. Alan Curbishley

Player B
1. Graeme Souness
2. Paul Harte
3. Preston
4. Richard Gough
5. Bristol City
6. Eric Cantona
7. Jim Jeffries
8. Newcastle United
9. Elm Park
10. Swansea City
11. Frank Sinclair
12. Egil Olsen
13. Bennett
14. Ray Clemence
15. Gary Plumley

Player A
1. Bryan Robson
2. Marco Branca
3. Paul Ince
4. Hamilton Ricard
5. Alen Boksic
6. Christian Ziege
7. Fabrizio Ravanelli
8. Gary Pallister
9. Ayresome Park

10. Malcolm Allison
11. Peter Taylor
12. John Hickton
13. Paul Merson
14. Brian Clough
15. Wilf Mannion

Player B
1. Don Revie
2. Paul Robinson
3. George Graham
4. Crystal Palace
5. Lee Chapman
6. Mark Viduka
7. Billy Bremner
8. Tomas Brolin
9. Bobby Collins
10. Raul
11. Peter Lorimer
12. Mick Jones
13. Norman Hunter
14. Nigel Martyn
15. Eric Cantona

Player A
1. Spurs
2. Stuart McCall
3. Watford
4. Clive Allen
5. Ian Rush
6. Southampton
7. 1985
8. Altrincham
9. George Curtis
10. Sheffield Wednesday
11. Luton Town
12. Bournemouth
13. Paul Allen
14. Telford United
15. 1982

Player B
1. Manchester United
2. Roberto di Matteo
3. Sutton United
4. Michael Thomas

5. Terry Venables
6. Howard Kendall
7. Paul Merson
8. Jeff Astle
9. Nottingham Forest
10. John Aldridge
11. Leicester City
12. Allan Clarke
13. White Hart Lane
14. Derby County
15. Ally MacLeod

MATCH 13   Round 4

Player A
1. Iceland
2. Luis Figo
3. John Toshack
4. Peter Schmeichel
5. Arnold Schwarzenegger
6. Borussia Moenchengladbach
7. Dennis Bergkamp
8. Dinamo Kiev
9. PSV Eindhoven
10. Rosenborg
11. Jean Pierre Papin
12. Valencia
13. Marcelo Salas
14. Gerd Muller
15. Johan Cruyff

Player B
1. George Graham
2. Peter Osgood
3. Stan Collymore
4. Leicester City
5. West Ham
6. Davor Suker/Patrick Vieira
7. Peter Lorimer
8. Norwich City
9. Kilmarnock
10. Martin Peters
11. Rotterdam
12. Eric Cantona
13. Gianfranco Zola
14. Hibernian
15. Leeds United

MATCH 13   Round 5

Player A
1. Didier Deschamps
2. Lothar Matthaus
3. Dennis Bergkamp
4. Poland
5. Peter Schmeichel
6. Paolo Maldini
7. Ferenc Puskas
8. Portugal
9. Rudi Voller
10. Franz Beckenbauer
11. Norway
12. Italy
13. Michel Platini
14. Czech Republic
15. Yugoslavia

Player B
1. Carlos Alberto
2. Claudio Tafferel
3. Mario Kempes
4. Uruguay
5. Zico
6. Peru
7. Romario
8. Gabriel Batistuta
9. Paraguay
10. Jairzinho
11. Carlos Valderrama
12. Cesar Luis Menotti
13. Claudio Caniggia
14. Silvinho
15. Rivaldo

MATCH 13   Round 6

Player A
1. Mark Crossley
2. Dennis Bergkamp
3. Andy Goram
4. Wolves
5. Dino Zoff
6. Biyik
7. Ian Rush
8. Brian Clough
9. Luxembourg

10. Jock Stein
11. Stuart Pearce
12. Peter Shilton
13. Terry Venables
14. West Brom
15. Terry Phelan

Player B
1. Dietmar Hamann
2. Manchester City
3. Referee
4. Peter Taylor
5. Scotland
6. Manchester
7. Bury
8. Rangers
9. Bobby Moore
10. Maurice Setters
11. Joe Baker
12. Adi Akinbiyi
13. Nottingham Forest
14. Tommy Docherty
15. Gary Pallister

MATCH 13
The Group Phase

Player A
1. Sweden
   Czechoslovakia
   Italy
2. Luis Figo
   Rivaldo
   Hristo Stoichkov
3. Ronnie Clayton
   Bobby Charlton
   Mick Channon
   Ray Clemence
   Trevor Cherry
   Sol Campbell

Penalty Shoot-out
1. Carl Cort
2. Liverpool
3. Reading
4. Gerry Hitchens
5. Paul Sturrock

Player B
1. Villa Park
   Hillsborough
   Bramall Lane
   Maine Road
2. Alaves
   Celta Vigo
   Barcelona
   Rayo Vallecano
3. Huddersfield
   Manchester City
   Manchester United
   Torino

Penalty Shoot-out
1. Nigel Spink
2. Brian McClair
3. Keith Gillespie
4. Bournemouth
5. Ron Greenwood

Player A
1. Arsene Wenger
2. Barry Hearn
3. Dion Dublin
4. Swindon Town
5. Sheffield United
6. Real Madrid
7. Eddie Newton
8. Leeds United
9. Gary Flitcroft
10. Lou Macari
11. Graeme Souness
12. Willie Young
13. Jimmy Frizzell
14. Andy Roxborough
15. Rangers

Player B
1. Alan Shearer
2. Steve Bruce
3. Jamie Carragher
4. Brian Clough
5. Des Walker
6. Rangers
7. John Aldridge
8. Branco
9. Ossie Ardiles
10. Nigel Worthington
11. George Reilly
12. Bradford City
13. Joe Miller
14. Gavin Peacock
15. Millwall

MATCH 14   Round 2

Player A
1. Steve Bull
2. Ade Akinbiyi
3. Dave Jones
4. Andy Gray
5. Graham Turner
6. Darren Ferguson
7. John De Wolf
8. Emlyn Hughes
9. Billy Wright
10. Tommy Docherty
11. Phil Parkes
12. Derek Dougan
13. Bill Slater
14. John Richards
15. Mike Bailey

Player B
1. The Hawthorns
2. Lee Hughes
3. Bryan Robson
4. Ron Atkinson
5. Kevin Kilbane
6. Canada
7. Laurie Cunningham
8. John Giles
9. Everton
10. 'Baggies'
11. Jeff Astle
12. David Mills
13. Tony Brown
14. Graham Williams
15. Cyrille Regis

MATCH 14   Round 3

Player A
1. Tranmere Rovers
2. George Graham
3. Bob Paisley
4. Newcastle United
5. Kenny Dalglish
6. Bryan Robson
7. David Pleat
8. Texaco Cup
9. Sunderland
10. Mervyn Day
11. Gary Lineker
12. Sunderland
13. Michael Robinson
14. West Ham United
15. Gordon Lee

Player B
1. Bryan Robson
2. Andy Townsend
3. Paul Bracewell
4. Roy Keane

5. Southampton
6. Chelsea
7. Paul Scholes
8. Billy Bonds
9. Bolton
10. Colchester United
11. Terry McDermott
12. Kevin Reeves
13. Herbert Chapman
14. Preston
15. Spurs

MATCH 14 Round 4

Player A
1. Bobby Charlton
2. Gabriel Batistuta
3. Eusebio
4. Parma
5. Monaco
6. ChristianVieri
7. Spurs
8. AC Milan
9. Marco Van Basten
10. Atletico Madrid
11. Ajax
12. Juan Veron
13. Celta Vigo
14. Inter Milan
15. Monaco

Player B
1. Tony Barton
2. Newcastle United
3. Alex Ferguson
4. Inter Milan
5. Jock Stein
6. Stewart Houston
7. Graeme Souness
8. Leeds United
9. Anderlecht
10. Stoke City
11. Gianluca Vialli
12. London
13. Liverpool
14. AC Milan
15. Barcelona

MATCH 14 Round 5

Player A
1. Mexico
2. Jack Taylor
3. Peter Bonetti
4. Peru
5. West Germany
6. Willie Johnstone
7. Jairzinho
8. Dino Zoff
9. Osvaldo Ardiles
10. East Germany
11. Gerd Muller
12. Brazil
13. Tunisia
14. Jan Tomasweski
15. Uwe Seeler

Player B
1. Jim Leighton
2. Toto Schillachi
3. Bulgaria
4. Paul Merson
5. Diego Maradona
6. Gabriel Batistuta
7. Ray Houghton
8. First game indoors
9. Frank Rijkaard/Rudi Voller
10. Laurent Blanc
11. Roberto Baggio
12. Walter Zenga
13. He was a linesman
14. Roy Aitken
15. Saudi Arabia

MATCH 14 Round 6

Player A
1. John Lukic
2. Gary Mabbutt
3. Wimbledon
4. Northampton Town
5. Ian Wright
6. Charlton Athletic
7. Jason McAteer
8. Peter Swales

9. Matthew Le Tissier
10. Diego Maradona
11. Sheffield United
12. Arsenal
13. Terry Hurlock
14. 1994
15. Swindon Town

Player B
1. Shaun Goater
2. Thierry Henry
3. Alan Smith
4. Romania
5. Ole Gunnar Solskjaer
6. Trevor Francis
7. Chris Waddle
8. Paul Davis
9. Luther Blissett
10. Bryan Robson
11. Reading
12. Stirling Albion
13. Andoni Goicoechea
14. Tony Ford
15. Joe Mercer

MATCH 14
The Group Phase

Player A
1. Anfield
   Old Trafford
   Hillsborough
   St James Park
   Elland Road
   City Ground
   Villa Park
2. France
   Italy
3. Bradford City
   Charlton
   Middlesbrough

Penalty Shoot-out
1. Chelsea
2. Wartime bomb
3. Kevin Pressman
4. 1981/2
5. Norway

Player B
1. Preston
   Sunderland
   Fulham
   West Ham
   Southampton
   QPR
2. Peterborough
   Birmingham City
   QPR
   Arsenal
3. Andy Cole
   Peter Beardsley

Penalty Shoot-out
1. Jack Charlton
2. Clive Allen
3. Gordon Strachan
4. France
5. Alan Shearer

MATCH 15   Round 1

Player A
1. Tony Adams
2. Christian Karambeu
3. Frank McAvennie
4. Charity Shield
5. Paul Gascoigne
6. Malcolm Macdonald
7. Dave Bassett
8. QPR
9. Steve Nicol
10. Jim McLean
11. Alan Hardaker
12. Scunthorpe United
13. The penalty spot
14. Spurs
15. Morton

Player B
1. Vinnie Jones
2. Marc Overmars
3. Alex Ferguson
4. Jimmy Greaves
5. Burnley
6. Aldo
7. Stuart McCall
8. St. Johnstone
9. Nottingham Forest
10. Watford
11. Hateley (Tony and Mark)
12. Scored for both sides
13. Chelsea
14. Walter Kidd
15. Emlyn Hughes

MATCH 15   Round 2

Player A
1. Matthew Le Tissier
2. Manchester United
3. Egil Soltvedt
4. Graeme Souness
5. Marian Pahars
6. Kevin Davies
7. Mick Channon
8. Nottingham Forest
9. Terry Paine
10. Ted Bates
11. Mick Channon
12. Ivan Golac
13. Ron Davies
14. Mark Wright
15. Chris Nicholl

Player B
1. Graham Rix
2. Terry Venables
3. John Gregory
4. Alan Knight
5. Alan Ball
6. Lee Bradbury
7. Tony Pulis
8. Ian St John
9. Andy Awford
10. Mark Hateley
11. Mick Quinn
12. Steve Foster
13. Kit Symons
14. Paul Mariner
15. Jimmy Dickinson

MATCH 15   Round 3

Player A
1. Bolton Wanderers
2. Crystal Palace
3. Bobby Stokes
4. Neville
5. Clive Allen
6. Nottingham Forest
7. Elton John
8. Newcastle United
9. Kidderminster Harriers
10. Andy Gray
11. Billy Bremner
12. Lee Martin
13. Last FA Cup second replay
14. Manchester United
15. Glen Roeder

Player B
1. Bolton Wanderers
2. Stanley Mortensen
3. Bobby Moore

4. Numbers
5. Crystal Palace
6. Don Revie
7. Dave Mackay
8. Gordon Banks
9. Robledo (George and Ted)
10. Cardiff City
11. Denis Compton
12. Jackie Milburn
13. Stan Cullis
14. Kennington Oval
15. Spurs

MATCH 15 Round 4

Player A
1. Matt Busby
2. Jesper Blomqvist
3. Denis Law
4. Les Sealey
5. Roy Keane
6. Bryan Robson
7. Juventus
8. David Beckham
9. Barcelona
10. Borussia Dortmund
11. Fenerbache
12. Anderlecht
13. Peter Schmeichel
14. Dwight Yorke
15. Sporting Lisbon

Player B
1. Joe Fagan
2. Phil Thompson
3. Four
4. 1977
5. Barcelona
6. Ian Rush
7. Dean Saunders
8. David Fairclough
9. John Wark
10. Steve McManaman
11. Graeme Souness
12. Nick Barmby
13. Roy Evans
14. Aberdeen
15. Roger Hunt

MATCH 15 Round 5

Player A
1. Germany
2. White City
3. Argentina
4. Pele
5. Chile
6. Mexico
7. Italy
8. Helmut Schoen
9. Eusebio
10. Bulgaria
11. Stade de France
12. Uruguay
13. Hungary
14. Argentina
15. Brazil

Player B
1. Walter Winterbottom
2. Michael Owen
3. Bobby Moore
4. Billy Wright
5. Jimmy Greaves
6. Turkey
7. Kerry Dixon
8. Paul Scholes
9. Andy Cole
10. Viv Anderson
11. Wales
12. Steve McManaman
13. Tim Flowers
14. Bryan Robson
15. Tony Adams

MATCH 15 Round 6

Player A
1. Sweden
2. Steve Stone
3. Brian Clough
4. Bobby Charlton
5. Swindon Town
6. Spurs
7. Steve Staunton
8. Mike England
9. Leeds United

10. Ronaldo
11. Steve Claridge
12. Gary Shaw
13. Manchester City
14. Anfield
15. Manchester United

Player B
1. Wrexham
2. Kenny Sansom
3. Arsenal
4. Steaua Bucharest
5. Rous Cup
6. Tommy Docherty
7. Colin Stein
8. Arnie Sidebottom
9. Partick Thistle
10. Alan Hansen
11. Angelo Peruzzi
12. Nayim
13. Anders Limpar
14. Ilie Dumitrescu
15. Bordeaux

MATCH 15
The Group Phase

Player A
1. Liverpool
   Aston Villa
   Arsenal
   Spurs
   West Ham
   Manchester United
2. Spain
   Italy
   Slovenia
   Yugoslavia
3. Leicester City
   Manchester City

Penalty Shoot-out
1. Michael Owen
2. Bolton
3. Craig Brown
4. Bill Nicholson
5. Reading

Player B
1. Denmark
   Holland
   Belgium
2. Blackburn Rovers
   Nottingham Forest
   Burnley
   Wolves
   Portsmouth
3. Chelsea
   Spurs
   QPR
   Crystal Palace

Penalty Shoot-out
1. Alan Hansen
2. Paul Gascoigne
3. Watford
4. Francis Lee
5. Cecare Maldini